The planet we live upon...was born some 4 or 5 billion years ago, and between that time and the present it has turned many very different faces to the sun. What is more, it continues to change even now, and will do so until it no longer spins in the sky.

THE CHANGING EARTH

- The theories and discoveries of the great geologists

- The nature of the atmosphere, the invisible envelope of air that engulfs the earth

- The nature of the hydrosphere, the rivers, ice fields, lakes and seas

- The lithosphere, the earth's rocky surface and inaccessible interior

- The properties of rocks and minerals

- The processes of weathering, soils and gravity

- The contribution of the great glaciers

- Vulcanism, volcanoes, diastrophism and earthquakes

- The evolution of plant and animal life

- The impact of Man, one of the mightiest agents of geological change

THE CHANGING EARTH

BANTAM SCIENCE AND MATHEMATICS

THE ATOM AND BEYOND
by E. Sheldon Smith

•

THE CHANGING EARTH
by Judith Viorst of Science Service, Inc.

•

GREAT IDEAS IN MODERN SCIENCE
by Robert W. Marks

•

MATHEMATICS TABLES AND HOW TO USE THEM
edited by Bradley V. Smith

•

THE NEW MATHEMATICS DICTIONARY AND HANDBOOK
by Robert W. Marks

•

THE NEW PHYSICS AND CHEMISTRY DICTIONARY
AND HANDBOOK
by Robert W. Marks

•

150 SCIENCE EXPERIMENTS STEP-BY-STEP
by Judith Viorst of Science Service, Inc.

•

ONE TWO THREE . . . INFINITY
by George Gamow

•

PROFILES OF THE FUTURE
by Arthur C. Clarke

•

RATS, LICE AND HISTORY
by Hans Zinsser

•

THE SEARCH FOR LIFE ON OTHER WORLDS
by David C. Holmes

•

WEATHER
by Armand N. Spitz

**BANTAM
SCIENCE
AND
MATHEMATICS**

The Changing Earth

by Judith Viorst of Science Service

Introduction by Frank C. Whitmore, Jr.

With a Preface by Watson Davis
Director Emeritus, Science Service

And Illustrations by Feodor Rimsky

THE CHANGING EARTH
Bantam Science and Mathematics Edition
published April 1967

*The photographs are reproduced through the courtesy of the follow-
ing sources: pages 26, 27, 33, 46 — Smithsonian Institution; 35, 36,
41, 43, 45 — Ward's Natural Science Establishment; 49, 50-51, 64,
66-67, 69, 88, 95, 110, 123 — United States Department of the Interior,
National Park Service; 56-57, 109, 120, 178-179 — United States Geo-
logical Survey; 70-71 — Bureau of Reclamation, Department of the
Interior; 73 — United States Department of Agriculture; 79 — J. E.
Haynes, St. Paul; 135, 147, 207, 224 — Science Service; 141 — United
States Navy; 192, 196, 197, 204, 212, 222, 228 — The American
Museum of Natural History.*

Library of Congress Catalog Card Number: 67-16074

Published simultaneously in the United States and Canada

PRINTED IN THE UNITED STATES OF AMERICA

To my sons
Anthony and Nicholas,
for whom I want this planet preserved

Acknowledgments

I want particularly to thank Dr. Frank Whitmore of the U.S. Geological Survey, without whose wisdom and kindness there would be no book. I shall always be grateful for his thoughtful understanding, his quick humor and his supreme patience.

Thanks, too, to Watson Davis, Anne Ewing, Margit Friedrich, Marcia Nelson, Dorothy Schriver, and Barbara Tufty of Science Service; to my husband, Milton Viorst; and to Mrs. Mary Louise Hawkins, who kept two small boys happily diverted while this book was being written.

JUDITH VIORST

Contents

Introduction *by Frank C. Whitmore, Jr.*		ix
Preface *by Watson Davis*		xi
1	Knowing the Earth	1
2	The Structure of the Earth	9
3	Minerals	19
4	Rocks	31
5	Weathering, Soils and Gravity	48
6	The Work of Flowing Streams	60
7	Water Under the Ground	80
8	Glaciers Shape the Land	93
9	Wind and the Deserts	106
10	The Shore and the Sea	116
11	Vulcanism and Volcanoes	132
12	Diastrophism and Earthquakes	145
13	The Making of Mountains	161
14	Unlocking the Past	172
15	The Paleozoic Era	186
16	The Mesozoic Era	200
17	The Cenozoic Era	215
18	Geology and Man	230
Table of Stratigraphic and Time Divisions		239
Bibliography		240
Index		242

Introduction

How do you explain the earth? What words can you use? Mathematics, chemistry and physics have specialized vocabularies that we accept because they represent new ideas to the beginner, and it is logical to learn new words for new ideas. But does geology need a special vocabulary and a whole book to explain it? After all, it deals with what we look at—and walk on—every day. If you hike or camp, you notice the details of the country in which you find yourself: the steep or gentle slope of valley walls, the nature of rock outcrops, the occurrence of fossils and of pebbles of many types. If you drive across even a few miles of country, you notice changes in the landscape and, if you observe carefully, you see that such changes can be related to the kinds of rocks present beneath the soil. The variety of the earth's surface is even more striking when seen from the air although, from a great altitude, the cause of the variety must usually be inferred rather than observed.

If you are in the habit of looking at the landscape you will, when reading this book, be like the bourgeois gentleman in Molière's play. He was astonished to discover that he had been speaking prose all his life; similarly, you will find that many of the concepts of geology are familiar to you even though the words are new. Then, as you go on with your study, you will realize why specialized terms are needed: nature presents infinite variety; and a variety of words is needed to express this. But nature is also orderly, and that is mainly what this book is about. If you want to learn how our environment is organized, and what you see when you are outdoors, this is a good place to start. When you are well into the book, go outdoors and look about you again. You will share one of the most exciting experiences of the natural scientist—the feeling of heightened powers of observation, based upon increased awareness of the world around you. You will find that world more complicated than you thought, but, if you understand something of its organization, its very complexity will become fascinating.

FRANK C. WHITMORE, JR.

U.S. Geological Survey
Washington, D.C.

Preface

The planet we live upon seems changeless and eternal, but it is neither. It was born some four or five billion years ago, and between that time and the present it has turned many very different faces to the sun. What is more, it continues to change even now, and will do so until it no longer spins in the sky.

This book describes the forces that mold the earth's changing face—water, wind, glaciers, vulcanism, diastrophism. It explains the making of our mountains and valleys and canyons, our beaches and caves and dunes, our waterfalls and geysers and springs. It also traces earth's history from its ambiguous beginnings through the shaping and reshaping of its continental features, telling—in rich detail—the awesome story of the evolution of life.

37 photographs and 30 drawings accompany the text, which is written for both the aspiring young geologist and anyone—of any age—curious about the planet on which he lives. The book abounds in facts about earth's past and present, but it also tempts the curious with the many unsolved questions that make geology a living, growing, ever-intriguing science.

WATSON DAVIS, Director Emeritus
Science Service

Chapter 1 / Knowing the Earth

About four centuries ago, Copernicus shook the world with his revolutionary pronouncement that the earth was not the stationary center of the universe, for the earth revolved around the sun. Nor was the sun, it subsequently turned out, the center of the universe either, but merely one of the many millions of stars forming a disk-shaped galaxy called the Milky Way. And the Milky Way, in turn, ceased to be regarded as the total universe when twentieth-century astronomers discovered evidence of an estimated one billion galaxies, known as island universes, distributed in space.

Placed in universal perspective, the earth seems hardly worthy of attention. From the point of view of its inhabitants, however, it has been a source of endless fascination since the first man-like animal scrabbled at the dirt beneath his feet and squinted bewildered eyes at a distant star.

THE GROWTH OF GEOLOGY

Geology is man's effort to explain the structure and origin of the earth and to study the successive changes in scene and life forms that have occurred throughout its history.

Geology is a young discipline, not even considered a science until the close of the eighteenth century. Its name was coined in 1778 by Jean André Deluc, who derived it from *geo,* meaning earth, and *logos,* meaning discourse.

Many of the observations on which geological principles are based, however, were made in the earliest days of human existence. Volcanoes, earthquakes and floods were noted; huge fossil bones were discovered; precious gems and metals were used as ornaments; and stones were fashioned into powerful weapons.

Almost every primitive culture endeavored—through legend and myth—to explain such phenomena. But the ancient Greeks left off myth-making to develop theories based on reasoning as well as observation.

The early natural philosophers, speculating on the shape of the earth, can probably be called our first geologists. Thales, who died about 550 B.C., believed that earth was a flat disk floating on water, while his contemporary, Anaximander, visualized a cylindrical planet. Anaximenes of Miletus (sixth century B.C.) said the earth was a disk afloat in the air; the Pythagoreans and Plato (427?–347 B.C.) believed it to be round; and Democritus (fifth century B.C.) pictured the earth and other heavenly bodies as sphere-shaped agglomerations of atoms. Aristotle (384–322 B.C.) also subscribed to the view that the earth was a sphere.

Herodotus (484?–425? B.C.) and Aristotle were among those ancient philosophers who early recognized one of the basic tenets of geology—the ever-changing nature of the earth's surface.

"The distribution of land and sea in particular regions," Aristotle wrote, "does not endure throughout all time, but it becomes sea in those parts where it was land and again it becomes land where it was sea. . . . As time never fails, and the universe is eternal, neither Tanais nor the Nile can have flowed forever. . . ."

The organic derivation of fossils, and the evolution of life from lower to higher forms, were other key geological concepts first considered hundreds of years before the Christian Era. Anaximander concluded from his study of fossils that fishes were the ancestors of mankind. Aristotle, too, understood that fossils were the remains of once-living organisms, and traced a steady, linear ascent from the lowly sponge and sea anemone to man.

The Greek historian and geographer Strabo (c. 63 B.C.—sometime after A.D. 21) was a highly observant traveler whose *Geography,* in 17 books, contains several references to geological subjects. Among the vast accumulation of detail are comments on minerals, mines, quarries, volcanoes and earthquakes.

Roman as well as Greek scholars helped to forward man's understanding of his earth. The poet Ovid (43 B.C. —A.D. 18) described many geologic processes in his *Metamorphoses.* The philosopher Seneca (c. 4 B.C.—A.D. 65) investigated fossils, volcanoes and the movements of the sea. Pliny the Elder (A.D. 23–79), noted historian and naturalist, produced a 37-volume *Natural History,* in which the real and the fanciful were intriguingly combined. The series included five semi-scientific books on minerals, within them a solemn statement that a diamond may be easily broken with a hammer if first soaked in the blood of a freshly killed goat. Pliny the Younger (A.D. 62– 113) provided a more important contribution to geology with his vivid descriptions of the eruption of Vesuvius and the earthquakes which accompanied that great disaster.

There were no significant advances in earth science during the sterile years between the death of the Roman Empire and the reawakening of the Renaissance.

Then, in the sixteenth century, the German scientist Georg Bauer (1494–1555), writing under the Latin name of Georgius Agricola, produced six books on geological subjects. His best-known works, *De re metallica* and *De natura fossilium,* have won him the title of Father of Mineralogy.

That perfect Renaissance man Leonardo da Vinci (1452–1519) also interested himself in geology. At a time when it was unpopular, perhaps even heretical, to think so, he maintained that fossils were organic in origin:

> When the floods from rivers turbid with fine mud deposited this mud over the creatures which live under the water near seashores, these animals remained pressed into the mud, and being under a great mass of this mud, had to die for lack of the animals on which they used to feed. And in the course of time, the sea sank, and the mud, being drained of the salt water, was eventually turned into stone. And the valves of such molluscs, their soft parts having already been consumed, were filled with mud; and as the surrounding mud became petrified, the mud which was within the shells, in contact with the former through their apertures, also became turned into stone.

But Leonardo's perceptive description of the forming of fossils was buried beneath the efforts of scholars to

force geology to conform to the literal teachings of the
Bible. According to the story of Creation in Genesis, God
did not bring forth life until the fabric of the earth had
been completed. How then could the remains of living
things be found within the earth's crust? For the logical
thinker there was only one answer—fossils were *not* the
remains of living things.

And so some people described them as the work of
an occult power—a spirit or *virtu divina*—whose intention
was to teach a moral lesson or to prophesize coming events.
Others held that fossils were developed by the powers of
evil for the purpose of deceiving mankind and leading it
into sin. Perhaps, it was suggested, emanations from the
stars and planets created these curious forms. Or might
they be the unsuccessful attempts of the Creator to produce
the earth's flora and fauna?

Some writers regarded fossils as the products of a fer-
mentation-like process which had occurred when the rocks
in which they were imbedded were in a soft and plastic
state. Many considered them jokes or "sports" of a per-
sonified Nature with a sense of humor. And one aesthete
suggested that they were created to ornament the inner
parts of the earth, just as tulips and roses were created
to adorn earth's surface.

At the beginning of the eighteenth century these no-
tions of the inorganic origin of fossils were finally discredited. Johann Beringer, a professor at the University of
Würzburg, had painstakingly collected and described a
remarkable array of fossils which he had come upon in
the neighboring regions. His discoveries included not only
marine and insect forms, but strange figures shaped like
the sun, the moon, and the letters of ancient alphabets.
It was not until he unearthed a fossil with his own name
traced upon it that the earnest professor realized that his
students, contemptuous of his foolish teachings, had manufactured and planted his great finds.

When it could no longer be denied that fossils had
once been living animals and plants, the theologians turned
to the story of Noah and the Deluge to reconcile geology
and Genesis. The ancient fossils, they declared, were the
remains of those who had perished in the biblical flood.
One Diluvialist, as the advocates of this theory were

called, explained that the "terrestrial globe was taken all to pieces and dissolved at the Deluge." Terrestrial matter settled down from the water in layers, he said, and marine bodies were "lodged in those Strata according to the Order of their Gravity."

Another Diluvialist published illustrations of what he described as "the bony skeleton of one of those infamous men whose sins brought upon the world the dire misfortune of the Deluge." But *Homo diluvii testis,* it was later revealed, was merely the skeleton of a salamander.

Despite these little setbacks, the study of geology moved forward.

Nicolaus Steno (1638–1687) a Latinized Dane, made a fundamental contribution to the science when he examined layers of sedimentary rock (strata) and observed that the lower layers were older than the upper. He also recognized that strata were originally deposited in a horizontal position but might become distorted through subsequent earth movements.

Steno's contemporary Robert Hooke (1635–1703) was an outstanding seventeenth-century geologist whose *Discourse of Earthquakes* dealt with volcanoes, the elevation of the land and other aspects of earth science. He also suggested that it might be possible to use fossils as a chronological index.

More than a century later, a sharp-eyed surveyor named William Smith (1769–1839) established the relationship between stratified rocks and the fossils which they contained. Traveling about the English countryside for many years, Smith noticed that strata always appeared in the same order—layers of coal beds below layers of chalk beds, for instance—unless they had been disturbed. He also noted that each layer of strata contained its own distinctive grouping of fossils. Smith's far-reaching and entirely original observations established the possibility of using fossils to determine the age of geological formations.

Abraham Gottlob Werner (1750–1817), professor of mineralogy at the Mining Academy of Freiberg, Germany, was one of the most influential and controversial figures in the history of geology. He investigated rocks and was the first to classify minerals systematically. He is best-known today, however, for his now-discredited theory of Neptunism, which maintained that the earth was originally a universal ocean from which all solid rocks —including granite and basalt—formed as precipitates.

The Neptunists were opposed by a group known as the Plutonists, who advanced the idea that granite and basalt originated from a molten state and not, as Werner maintained, as marine precipitates. Leader of the Plutonists was James Hutton (1726–1797), today considered the founder of modern scientific geology.

In Hutton's day the doctrine of catastrophism, popular for centuries in a variety of forms, still prevailed among geologists. This doctrine asserted that at various times throughout earth's history catastrophes (like the biblical flood) brought about violent and sudden changes —the raising of mountains, the carving of canyons, the submergence of continents, the annihilation of life.

Hutton observed the inexorable work of wind, water and weather on crumbling rock, and visualized an endless vista of time in which he could see "no vestige of a beginning, no prospect of an end." Given time enough, he reasoned, these natural forces could erode a continent. He concluded that all the geological phenomena of the past were the result of processes still operative today. This was his famous doctrine of uniformitarianism which said, in effect, that the present is the key to the past.

The persuasiveness of Hutton's logic in his *Theory of the Earth* won many adherents, but it did not banish catastrophism. Uniformitarianism required a vaster period of time than most scholars could accept. And the rejection of the catastrophe explanation seemed to reject Noah's flood as well, which was contrary to religious teachings. Baron Georges Cuvier (1769–1832), a renowned student of fossil animals, was the most famous of the scholars who continued to explain past earth history in terms of world-wide cataclysms.

Eventually the theory of uniformitarianism won general acceptance, thanks largely to the efforts of Sir Charles Lyell (1797–1875). His classic work bore the lengthy but informative title of *Principles of Geology, Being an Attempt to Explain the Former Changes of the Earth's Surface by Reference to Causes Now in Operation.* Described by a colleague as "sufficiently important to mark almost a new era in the progress of our science," the study had a profound impact on geological thinking in the late nineteenth and early twentieth centuries.

> When we are unable to explain the monuments of past changes [wrote Sir Charles], it is always more probable that the difference arises from our ignorance of all the existing agents, or all their possible effects in an indefinite lapse of time, than that some cause was formerly in operation which has ceased to act. . . . Our estimate, indeed, of the value of all geological evidence, and the interest derived from the investigation of earth's history, must depend entirely on the degree of confidence which we feel in regard to the permanency of the laws of nature. . . .

THE SCOPE OF GEOLOGY

There have been many great geologists since the days of Hutton and Lyell, but they tend more and more to be specialists. For as knowledge has increased, the science of geology has been divided into several fields.

A basic distinction is made between *physical geology* and *historical geology*. The first investigates the materials of the earth and the processes that act upon them. The second seeks to trace the history of the earth from its earliest beginnings.

A number of divisions are based on more specific subject matter:

Petrology (as well as *petrography* and *petrogenesis*) deals with the origin, description and classification of rocks.

Structural geology examines the positions and relationships of rocks and the forces that deform or break them.

Stratigraphy is the study of layered rocks.

Geomorphology investigates the origin and development of land forms.

Geochemistry is the study of the chemistry of rocks, waters and atmosphere.

Geodesy is concerned with measuring the size and shape of the earth.

Geophysics applies the principles of physics to the

study of the earth and includes such branches as *seismology,* the study of earthquakes.

Mineralogy is the study of minerals.

Oceanography deals with oceans and their basins.

Meteorology is the study of the atmosphere.

Cosmogony covers the early history of earth and the various hypotheses about earth's origins.

Paleontology is the study of fossils, and may be subdivided into *paleobotany,* the study of fossil plants, and *paleozoology,* the study of fossil animals.

Applied geology also has its specialties, including *economic geology* (the study of the commercial uses of the resources of the earth), *agricultural geology* (the study of soils), and *engineering geology* (the study of the relationship between the earth's crust and man-made structures).

Although geology, with its many branches, is an independent science, it is intimately related to other disciplines. Chemistry and physics, astronomy and biology, geography and anthropology, economics and mathematics —all are drawn upon to enlarge man's understanding of his planet.

THE MEANING OF GEOLOGY

Some believe that the goal of science is the acquisition of knowledge about everything under (and beyond) the sun. Others believe that science's goal is to increase the well-being of humanity. Geology serves both ends.

Economically, geologists have discovered and exploited the resources of the earth for a multitude of uses —as fuels, jewels, metals, fertilizers, abrasives and structural materials. Geological data have been utilized in the planning of highways and bridges, dams and artificial lakes, flood-control and drainage systems.

Intellectually, geology has profoundly altered man's view of the world. Although it is sometimes said that we know more about the moon than we know of the earth, we have come a long way from ancient myths and eighteenth-century cataclysms. Modern geology has given us another perspective with which to look at the world—the perspective of time.

Chapter 2 / The Structure of the Earth

A camera in the sky photographs earth as a bland and even-featured planet, its towering peaks and cutting valleys smoothed flat. It is always startling to be reminded that the distance between the tip of Mount Everest and the lowest known ocean depth is only a little more than a dozen miles.

Scientists have made many measurements of the earth. Its near-sphere shape (more precisely called an oblate spheroid) has a 7900-mile diameter from pole to flattened pole, and a diameter of 7927 miles at its bulging equator. Its equatorial circumference, they have found, is approximately 24,900 miles, its surface area 197 million square miles, its volume slightly more than 250 billion cubic miles, its mass an estimated 6,600 quintillion tons.

The structure of the earth is tripartite, with a region of gases (the atmosphere), a region of water (the hydrosphere), and a solid region (the lithosphere). There is some intermingling of air and water and rock, but basically each region is separate from the others and each has its own distinctive characteristics.

THE ATMOSPHERE

The invisible envelope of air that engulfs the earth produces a profound effect upon earth's surface. Life, for instance, except for a very primitive kind, would be impossible without air. Air is responsible for our weather —for fog, snow, hail, clouds and wind. It is responsible, too, for dawn and twilight, fire and rust, odor and sound, and the blue skies overhead. It serves as a thermal blanket, helping to retain the heat received from the sun, and as a shield against deadly radiation.

The ancient Greeks regarded air as one of the four "elements" of the universe (together with fire, water and earth) but its constituents were not identified until the past 200 years. Today we know that the composition of the atmosphere is basically nitrogen (78.03%) and oxygen (20.99%), with argon, carbon dioxide, hydrogen, neon, helium, krypton, xenon, water vapor, smoke particles, dust and plant spores also present. These substances form, not a chemical compound, but a mechanical mixture. The basic gases maintain essentially the same properties at different times and in different places, while the so-called "impurities" and water vapor vary sharply.

The atmosphere has tremendous weight, exerting a downward pressure of 14.7 pounds to the square inch at every point on the earth's surface at sea level. A square foot of earth, then, is oppressed by 2016 pounds, while the entire mass of air is 5,900,000,000,000,000 tons. Human beings are not squashed flat by this great burden because their body fluids and dissolved gases are in equilibrium with it.

Air is highly compressible, and its density is by no means uniform. Heaviest at lower altitudes, air pressure decreases as you climb. At an altitude of about 14 miles, the barometer reads only 0.6 inch, indicating that a full 96% of the atmosphere, by weight, is distributed beneath that point. No one knows how far the remaining 4% extends. The earth's atmosphere may be hundreds or it may be thousands of miles thick. Its outermost limit, physicists have calculated, is some 20,000 miles, beyond which gas molecules could no longer be held captive by the force of earth's gravity.

Like air pressure, air temperature also decreases with altitude, because the atmosphere receives most of its heat from the earth rather than from the direct rays of the sun. The average temperature drop on an upward climb is 1° F for each 300 feet.

This steady decline halts abruptly at the tropopause, which is found at 11 miles above the equator and at 4 or 5 miles above the poles. The tropopause serves as the cut-off point of the atmosphere's bottom layer—the troposphere—where changeable winds, storms, snow and rain occur. Beyond is the stratosphere, a calm, cold, dry, cloudless region undisturbed by dust, water vapor or turbulent movements of the air. Within this middle layer, the temperature rises for a while, but at its outer boundary— about 50 miles up—the thermometer drops to a chilly $-150°$ F. Then follows the immense top layer of the atmosphere, the ionosphere, which reaches, at some unknown point, to the borderlands of space.

THE HYDROSPHERE

The waters of the hydrosphere are found in the sea, in the atmosphere, in glaciers and ice fields, in rivers and lakes and running streams, and in the crust of the earth. Our present knowledge of the solar system indicates that this planet is unique in its possession of large quantities of liquid water.

Water is a simple compound—two atoms of hydrogen linked with a single atom of oxygen—yet its properties are unusual indeed.

Fresh water freezes at $0°$ C or $32°$ F. Like other substances, including salt water, it contracts as it cools— to a point. Then, shortly before it freezes, it reaches maximum density, and as the temperature drops from $4°$ C to $0°$ C, the water expands about 9%. Because of this remarkable property of expansion on cooling, lakes will freeze on the surface instead of bottom-to-top, and ice (less dense than liquid water) will float.

Water is the only substance found on earth's surface as a solid, a liquid and a gas. Its capacity to absorb and transmit heat has a crucial moderating effect on the temperatures of the world. Its ability to support a great range of plant and animal forms makes it one of the leading food suppliers. And it is, of course, the source of life-nourishing rain through the water it gives up to the atmosphere.

Water also serves a vital function as a universal solvent. Each year the sea receives from inflowing rivers some 2¾ billion tons of solids dissolved from rocks and soil. These dissolved substances, including the familiar sodium chloride with which we salt our food, are responsible for the salinity of the sea.

The sea is the primary component (about 95%) of the hydrosphere. Waters cover approximately 71% of the earth's surface—a total of 139,400,000 square miles—as compared to the 57,500,000 square miles (29%) of land area. The land and the sea are very unevenly distributed, with 80% of earth's land encircling the North Pacific, the North Atlantic and the Arctic oceans, while 90% of earth's water is found in the Indian, South Pacific and South Atlantic oceans.

THE LITHOSPHERE

The lithosphere is composed of earth's rocky surface and its highly inaccessible interior. The behavior of earthquake waves, which change in velocity according to the nature of the material through which they pass, indicates that the lithosphere consists of three major zones differing in composition, density, elasticity and, perhaps, state. Because the waves are reflected and bent at the boundaries between the zones, these boundaries are called discontinuities. The Mohorovicic (or Moho or M-) discontinuity, at a depth of 20 to 30 miles, separates the earth's outer zone—the crust—from its intermediate zone—the mantle. At a depth of 1800 miles the Wiechert-Gutenberg discontinuity separates the mantle from earth's inner zone—the core.

Uplifted mountain areas have provided man with a view of rocks that once existed at depths of several miles. But efforts to penetrate earth's interior have yielded limited results. The deepest oil wells cut just slightly more than 4 miles into the earth, and the deepest mine shafts bore less than 10,000 feet.

These wells and mines indicate, however, that earth's temperature increases with depth at an average rate of about 1° F for every 60 feet. The heat inside the earth is due, in part, to the radioactivity of certain rocks, which produce heat when their uranium changes to lead. Another source of earth's high temperature is pressure, which also increases with depth. Thus the pressure of crust on mantle heats the mantle, while the greater pressure of mantle on core makes the core even hotter.

The Crust The crust of the earth is dominated by two major features—the continental blocks and the ocean basins. An underlayer of the black, heavy rock called basalt is present throughout the ocean basins and underlies the continents. The basic material of the continental blocks is granite, lighter in color and density.

The granitic materials of the crust are called sial, a made-up word taken from the first two letters of silicon and aluminum, the elements which are most abundant in granite. The basaltic materials of the crust are known as sima, taken from the chief constituents of basalt—the elements silicon and magnesium.

The ratio between the densities of granite and basalt is comparable to that between ice and water. Thus the granitic continental masses are, in effect, floating in the heavier basalt.

The continents which we know are merely the exposed dry-land areas of the great oval or shield-shaped continental masses. Present off almost every coast are the shallowly submerged margins of the continents, sometimes as wide as several hundred miles, sometimes measurable in inches. These continental shelves, as they are called, angle downward into the sea at a gentle 10–20 feet to the mile. But at their outer edges—at depths averaging 600 feet—there is an abrupt, steep drop, known as the continental slope, which reaches down into the basalt ocean basins.

The continents rise above sea level to an average height of little more than ½ mile, with a maximum elevation of 5½ miles. The average depth of the ocean basins is 2½ miles, their maximum 6½.

The continents and basins are called first-order relief features because they are the most conspicuous topographic forms on the face of the earth. Plains, plateaus and mountains (which are present within the ocean basins as well as on dry land) are second-order relief features. Of lesser importance are such formations as U-shaped valleys, sand dunes and other diversities of the scenery —third-order relief features all.

The Mantle The earth's crust rests on the denser material of the mantle which lies beneath the Moho discontinuity. The upper part of the mantle appears to resemble a heavy rock called peridotite. The inner part of

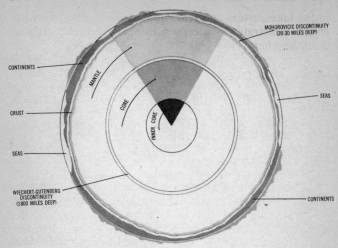

Earth's lithosphere is composed of an outer
zone called the crust, an intermediate zone called
the mantle, and an inner zone called the core.

the mantle, with its greater density, may have the same
composition as an iron-nickel alloy.

The Core The core of the earth is presumed to consist of two parts—an outer molten core and an inner
solid core. Its diameter is about 4300 miles and its volume
is one-eighth that of the earth. The materials which com-
pose the core—or part of it—are probably an iron-nickel-
cobalt combination. The average density of the core is
about 12, but at the very center the density may be more
than 17, and the pressure may be three million times the
pressure at the surface. Many scientists attribute the origin
of earth's magnetic field to the electric currents generated
by the motion of the liquid core.

GEOLOGIC PROCESSES

Near the surface of the earth, the atmosphere, hydrosphere and lithosphere intermingle. The atmosphere holds
water vapor from the hydrosphere, while air is dissolved

in the lakes, rivers and seas. Both atmosphere and hydrosphere penetrate, to a certain extent, the rocky crust of the lithosphere.

The landscape of earth's surface is altered because of this intermingling. Water, wind and ice wear down, carry away and build up. The wearing down process may function statically, through the forces of weathering, which decay or disintegrate rocks. Erosion is a more active process of wearing down, although the word is sometimes used to mean the work of carrying away as well. Lowering of the earth's surface through erosion is termed degradation. The moving of decomposed and disintegrated rock and rock-forming materials from one place to another is known as transportation. The laying down of these transported materials is deposition, and the building up of earth's surface by this activity is aggradation.

All these geologic processes are external, for their agents are weather, flowing streams, ground water, glaciers, wind and sea. But there are also internal forces, originating far beneath the surface of the earth, which determine the configuration of its face.

The two basic geological processes operating within the earth are vulcanism and diastrophism. Vulcanism, which is responsible for volcanoes, includes all movements of molten rock and the formation of solid rock from a molten state. Diastrophism, which is responsible for earthquakes, involves movements of the solid parts of the earth which cause the earth's displacement and deformation.

ISOSTASY

Despite the constant shifting of materials upon the earth's surface, earth maintains a state of gravitational equilibrium known as isostasy. According to the principle of isostasy, there is a condition of balance between adjacent portions of earth's crust, or a tendency for balance to be restored if disturbed.

The theory of isostasy postulates that any extensive area of the earth, if cut out like an ice cream cone from surface to core, would weigh the same as any other segment of equal surface area, even if one segment were cut

ISOSTASY 1

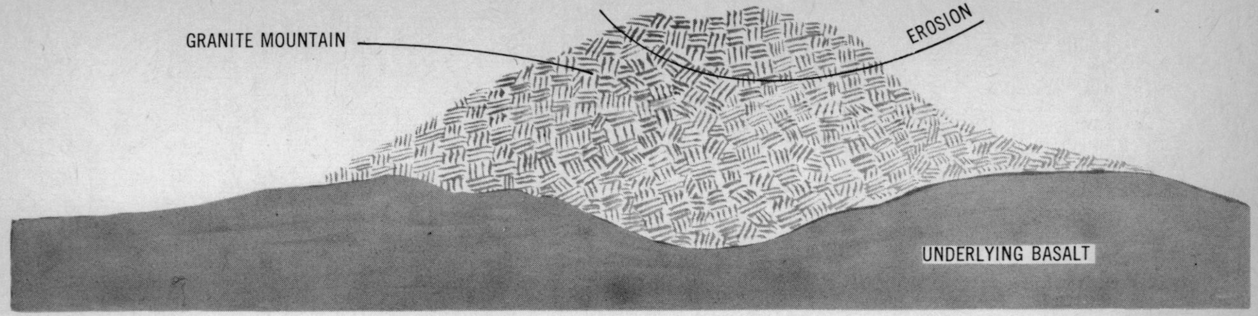

GRANITE MOUNTAIN

EROSION

UNDERLYING BASALT

ISOSTASY 2

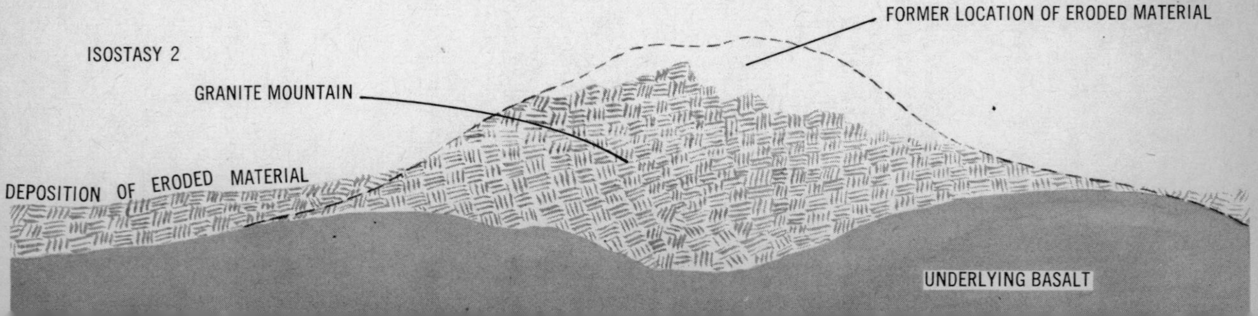

GRANITE MOUNTAIN

FORMER LOCATION OF ERODED MATERIAL

UNDERLYING BASALT

DEPOSITION OF ERODED MATERIAL

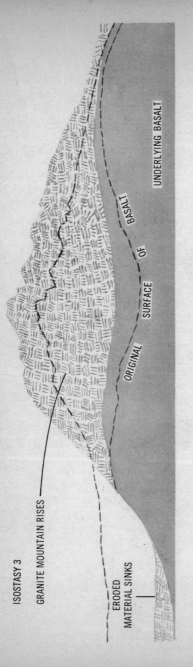

ISOSTASY 3

GRANITE MOUNTAIN RISES

ORIGINAL SURFACE OF BASALT

UNDERLYING BASALT

ERODED MATERIAL SINKS

The theory of isostasy postulates that an extensively eroded section of earth rises slowly, while an overloaded section of earth sinks slowly.

from the top of a mountain and another from the bottom of the sea. It is known, for instance, that mountains are not merely a load of material sitting upon a crust that is everywhere uniform in density. Instead, mountains have roots composed of the same granitic materials which make up the basic rock of the exposed mountain regions. These roots penetrate deep into the underlying basalt, so that the rock beneath high mountains is less dense than that underlying adjacent plains, where the heavier basalt is much closer to the surface. Mountain roots are the most dramatic example of nature's scheme of compensation, whereby differences in elevation above sea level are balanced by a variation in density of the materials below sea level.

The theory of isostasy further postulates that an overloaded section of earth slowly sinks, while an extensively eroded section slowly rises. Thus, when material is removed from the top of a mountain by erosion, the crust will become elevated—just as the base of an iceberg becomes elevated when its top is melted away. If, on the other hand, a heavy deposit of eroded mountain material accumulates in the lowlands, these lands will sink because of the added weight.

A LOOK AHEAD

The following chapters will examine the rocks and minerals that make up earth's crust, and the geologic forces which act upon them, building mountains and washing them away, shaping canyons and valleys, deserts, plains and plateaus, and shifting the boundaries between the land and the sea. In the final chapters the emphasis will be on earth's geological history—from its emergence as a planet some five billion years ago to its present shaky dominance by man.

Chapter 3 / Minerals

The dark, pale, vivid, speckled, patchy, grainy, smooth rocks of earth's lithosphere vary so greatly in appearance that it seems, sometimes, unreasonable to characterize them all with one general term. But each of these rocks shares a common unifying feature—it is composed of one or more basic substances called minerals.

WHAT ARE MINERALS?

While the minerals which make up rocks are not always present in the same proportions, minerals themselves are essentially uniform in composition. They are always naturally occurring substances—never synthetics. They usually have an internal geometric structure, which is often expressed in outward crystal forms. They are generally chemical compounds consisting of two or more elements in combination, but a few uncombined elements—such as copper, sulfur and carbon—are also minerals.

ELEMENTS, ATOMS AND MOLECULES

Elements are substances that cannot be separated into simpler forms of matter by ordinary means. Of the 103 presently known elements, approximately 90 are found in the crust of the earth. Eight of these 90 are vastly more abundant than the rest, adding up to almost 99% of the whole.

The eight predominant elements are oxygen (chemical symbol O) 46.59%; silicon (Si) 27.72%; aluminum (Al) 8.13%; iron (Fe) 5.01%; calcium (Ca) 3.63%; sodium

(Na) 2.85%; potassium (K) 2.60%; and magnesium (Mg) 2.09%. It is clear from these figures that three-quarters of the lithosphere consists of silicon and oxygen. Most of earth's minerals, then, are chemical compounds made up of these two elements in combination with the other six.

Combined elements can be represented by chemical symbols in a chemical formula. Each symbol represents one atom of an element, while the formula represents a distinctive grouping of these atoms to form a molecule. (Note: An atom is the smallest fraction of an element that can exist by itself and still show the element's chemical qualities. A molecule is the smallest fraction of a substance that can be obtained without altering the substance's composition or characteristics.)

A chemical formula is either rigidly fixed or varies according to a dependable law. In either case, it states the kind and number of atoms required to form a given material. The mineral halite (sodium chloride), for instance, is represented by the formula NaC1. This formula says, in chemical shorthand, that one atom of the element sodium (Na) and one atom of the element chlorine (C1) will unite to form one molecule of sodium chloride. Other formulas are considerably more complex, with the mineral hornblende represented by an imposing $Ca_2Na(Mg,Fe)_4$ $(Al,Fe,Ti)_3Si_6O_{22}(O,OH)_2$.

PROPERTIES OF MINERALS

Because each mineral has its own chemical composition and atomic structure, each has its own characteristic physical properties. The geologist identifies a mineral by its color, streak, luster, hardness, specific gravity, structure, crystal form, cleavage and fracture.

Color Some minerals are always the same color, while others vary from specimen to specimen. Thus one mineral may be readily identified by its color, while the color of another may provide no clue at all.

Among the distinctive and reliable colors that aid in mineral identification are the blue of azurite, the green of malachite and the vivid yellow of sulfur. Many minerals, however, are basically colorless, and appear white unless tinted by impurities. Fluorite, for instance, may be tinted violet, blue or rose. White quartz will turn smoky when traces of carbon are present, and with manganese will become the gemstone amethyst.

Because air and moisture tend to alter color, it may be necessary to break a rock in order to see the true colors of its minerals. Sometimes the specimen must be reduced to a powder before its true color is revealed.

Streak The color of a mineral in a finely powdered form is called its streak. A streak can also be obtained by scratching a mineral on the white unglazed back of a piece of tile. In some cases streak may be more helpful than color in identifying a mineral.

A streak may be the same color as the mineral, a paler version of it, or entirely different. Silver-gray galena gives a silver-gray streak. Blue azurite streaks light-blue. But hematite, even in its steel-gray variety, will show a characteristic red-brown streak.

Luster A mineral's luster is the way in which ordinary light is reflected from its surfaces. Minerals may be broadly divided into two groups—those having a look of polished metals (metallic luster) and those having a non-metallic luster.

In the non-metallic group are minerals with lusters that speak for themselves—silky, pearly, resinous, greasy or earthy. Minerals that look like glass have a vitreous (glassy) luster. Minerals with an adamantine (diamond-like) luster are very brilliant.

Hardness A very useful identifying feature of a mineral is its hardness. Since weather will alter the hardness of a mineral on the outside, it should be broken so that it can be tested on an inside surface.

Over a hundred years ago Friedrich Mohs devised a hardness scale which still serves to indicate the relative hardness of minerals. The scale is based on the principle that a harder mineral will scratch a softer one and minerals of equal hardness will barely scratch each other. The Mohs scale indicates a mineral's rank in a hierarchy, not its amount of hardness in any absolute sense. For instance, number 9 (corundum) is not three times as hard as number 3 (calcite), and the interval between corundum and diamond is greater than all the rest of the scale combined. Below is the Mohs hardness scale.

1. Talc. Minerals with a hardness of 1 are the softest of all minerals and can be scratched with the fingernail.

2. Gypsum. Minerals like gypsum can also be scratched with the fingernail, but it is necessary to press harder.

3. Calcite. A sharp-edged copper penny will scratch minerals with the hardness of calcite.

4. Fluorite. Not a penny but a knife is required to scratch minerals with a hardness of 4. Such minerals will not scratch glass.

5. Apatite. Minerals with a hardness of 5 cannot easily be scratched with a knife. They can scratch ordinary glass.

6. Orthoclase feldspar. This and other minerals with a hardness of 6 cannot be scratched by a knife. They will scratch glass.

7. Quartz. Minerals of this hardness scratch glass easily.

8. Topaz. Minerals like topaz are able to scratch quartz.

9. Corundum. These minerals will scratch topaz.

10. Diamond. This is by far the hardest mineral and can scratch all others.

Specific Gravity   The specific gravity of a mineral is the ratio of its weight to that of an equal volume of water. The specific gravity of pure water is 1. If a mineral's specific gravity is greater than 1, it is heavier than water. If the specific gravity is less than 1, the mineral is lighter than water and will float.

The specific gravity of different minerals varies greatly, but most familiar non-metallic minerals in earth's crust fall between 2.5 and 3.0. There are several instruments which can determine specific gravity, but differences between different specimens can be detected by "heft."

Structure Minerals show wide differences in gross structure. Some of the forms in which they occur are described as massive, fibrous and columnar.

Crystal Form Minerals tend to crystallize into definite, characteristically shaped crystals, bounded by smooth planes called crystal faces. The angles between the corresponding faces of any given mineral always remain the same, regardless of size. When crystal faces are present, their shapes and interfacial angles serve to identify the mineral.

All crystals can be placed in one of six major crystal systems. These are isometric, tetragonal, hexagonal, orthorhombic, monoclinic and triclinic. A well-known example of hexagonal crystals is the snowflake, which exhibits innumerable variations on a six-sided theme.

A mineral's outward crystal form reflects an internal structure produced by the orderly geometric arrangement of its atoms. The opposite is not necessarily true. That is, a mineral's orderly internal structure may not be represented by an external crystal appearance. Therefore, not all minerals with an orderly internal structure are crystals.

Some minerals do not have an orderly internal structure. Such minerals are said to be amorphous.

All crystals can be placed in one of six major crystal systems—monoclinic (1), triclinic (2), *(turn page)* isometric (3), tetragonal (4), hexagonal (5), or orthorhombic (6).

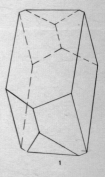

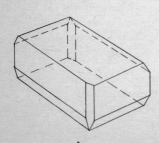

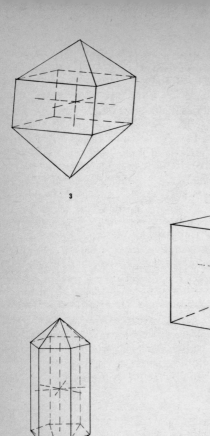

3

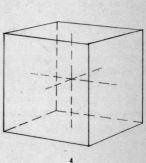

4

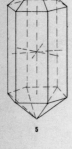

5

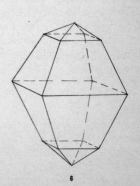

6

(It is important to note that the fundamental difference between minerals is not their chemical composition but their internal structure. Both diamond and graphite are pure carbon, but due to the arrangement of their atoms the first is hard and transparent, the second soft, greasy and opaque.)

Cleavage Like the crystal form of minerals, cleavage is a property determined by the geometric arrangement of atoms in a mineral. Cleavage is the ability of some minerals to break (or cleave) along smooth planes that parallel each other.

Some minerals—like mica—have only one cleavage and can be split into countless thin parallel flakes. Many minerals have two cleavages; others have three or more. The number of cleavages and the angles between them are always characteristic for a particular mineral.

Fracture When a mineral has no cleavage, it breaks irregularly, with a fracture. A fracture may be conchoidal (shell-like), like the fracture of quartz, obsidian and ordinary glass. It may be hackly (jagged-edged), like the fractures seen on copper. A fracture may also be described as splintery, fibrous, irregular, uneven, even or earthy.

Others Many other physical properties are useful in identifying minerals, although the ones mentioned above are of chief importance. Some minerals are attracted by a magnet, some are not; some "fluoresce" or glow colorfully when submitted to ultraviolet light; some display striations on cleavage surfaces or crystal faces. Minerals differ, too, in ability to conduct electricity, in fusibility, solubility and reactions to chemicals.

COMMON ROCK-FORMING MINERALS

Only a few of the earth's 2000 or so minerals are rock-forming. Several minerals may comprise a single rock. Granite, for instance, will show light-gray areas of quartz and feldspar as well as black specks of biotite.

Minerals containing an element combined with oxy-

Six-sided quartz crystals terminated at each end by a sharp-pointed pyramid.

Hornblende is commonly dark green to black; here it is mixed with white calcite.

gen are called oxides. Quartz is the most common of all. Minerals containing sulfur and oxygen, plus other elements, are sulfates. Gypsum is the most common. There are also carbonates (such as calcite)—compounds of carbon, oxygen and at least one additional element; halides (such as halite)—compounds including chlorine, fluorine, bromine or iodine; and, most numerous, the silicates (such as the feldspar group, the mica group and the ferromagnesian silicates). These important rock-forming minerals will be described below.

Quartz [SiO_2] When pure, quartz is clear and colorless, but it also exists as flint (black), rose quartz (pink), amethyst (violet) and other colorful varieties. It breaks with a conchoidal fracture, gives off a vitreous-to-greasy luster, has a hardness of 7 and a specific gravity of 2.65. Allowed to grow unencumbered, quartz crystallizes in six-sided crystals terminated at each end by a sharp-pointed pyramid. Quartz crystals sometimes reach dimensions of over a foot, but in rocks like granite they seldom measure more than ½ inch in diameter. Quartz may be found in granites, gneisses and sandstones.

Other oxides are such ore minerals as hematite, magnetite, limonite and bauxite. Water is an oxide of hydrogen.

Gypsum [$CaSO_4 \cdot 2H_2O$] Gypsum is colorless or white, but may be other colors when impure. Its luster is vitreous to pearly or silky. It has tabular crystals and three cleavages—one perfect, the others not nearly as good. It has a hardness of 2 and a specific gravity of 2.2–2.4. The name gypsum refers both to the mineral and to the rocks that consist of this mineral alone.

Other sulfates are barite and anhydrite.

Calcite [$CaCO_3$] This abundant mineral sometimes forms a rock all by itself. Limestone, for instance, and marble, are not aggregations of minerals but the single compound calcium carbonate. Calcite is usually colorless, white or yellow, but impurities may turn it any number of other shades. The mineral has a dull-to-vitreous luster, "dogtooth" or flat crystals and three perfect cleavages at oblique angles. Its hardness is 3; its specific gravity, 2.72.

Dolomite and siderite are other carbonates.

Halite [NaC1]   This mineral is common salt, colorless to white unless tinted by impurities. It has a vitreous luster and is distinguished by its salty taste. Halite crystals are cubic, and its three excellent cleavages form right angles. Halite has a hardness of 2–2.5 and a specific gravity of 2.1.

Fluorite is also a halide.

The Feldspar Group   Feldspars are combinations of potassium, or sodium and calcium, with oxygen, aluminum, and silicon. They are the most abundant of the rock-forming minerals, making up at least 50% of the lithosphere, and are common in all igneous rocks. Orthoclase and plagioclase are representative feldspars.

1.   Light-gray or pinkish orthoclase [$KAlSi_3O_8$] forms box-like crystals and has a well-developed cleavage in two directions—both intersecting at a 90° angle. Its luster is pearly or vitreous. This feldspar has a hardness of 6 and a specific gravity of 2.5–2.6.

2.   Plagioclase [$NaAlSi_3O_8$ to $CaAl_2Si_2O_8$] also has a hardness of 6 and a vitreous to pearly luster. It is usually white or pale gray but may sometimes show an opalescent play of colors. It has well-formed crystals and two good cleavages at approximately right angles. Specific gravity is 2.6–2.7.

The Mica Group   These minerals have a sheet-like arrangement of atoms. The most important rock formers in the mica group are muscovite and biotite, common in granites, schists and shales.

1.   Muscovite [$KAl_3Si_3O_{10}(OH)_2$], called white mica, is generally colorless, although gray, green or light-brown pieces may be found. Muscovite has a pearly-to-vitreous luster. Its crystals are thin and scale-like, and in one direction of cleavage it yields very thin flaky scales—its most distinctive characteristic. The hardness of muscovite is 2–3; specific gravity, 2.8–3.1.

2.   Biotite [$K(Mg,Fe)_3AlSi_3O_{10}(OH)_2$] is called black mica and is commonly dark brown or black. In granite it occurs as shining, jet-black flakes. Biotite has a pearly-to-vitreous luster and perfect scales in one direction of cleavage. Its hardness is 2.5–3; its specific gravity is

2.7–3.2. The crystals of biotite are thin and scaly and commonly six-sided.

The Ferromagnesian Silicates The darker minerals of rocks—the amphibole group, the pyroxene group and the mineral olivine—are included in this category. These minerals contain iron and magnesium, and are found in the darker and more basic igneous rocks.

1. Hornblende [$Ca_2Na(Mg,Fe)_4(Al,Fe,Ti)_3Si_6O_{22}(O,OH)_2$] is the most familiar member of the amphibole group of ferromagnesian silicates. It is commonly dark green to black, sometimes shining like jet in an unweathered state. Its luster is strongly vitreous and its prismatic crystals are long, narrow and six-sided. This mineral shows a distinctive cleavage pattern—with two good cleavages meeting at angles of 56° and 124°. Specific gravity is 2.9–3.2; hardness is 5–6.

2. Like the amphiboles, the pyroxene group of ferromagnesian silicates is dark green or black with a vitreous-to-dull luster. Pyroxenes have short, eight-sided, stubby crystals and two cleavages that intersect at approximately right angles. Hardness is 5–6; specific gravity is 3.2–3.6. Augite is the most common variety.

3. Olivine [$(Fe,Mg)_2SiO_4$] has a green color and a vitreous luster. Its glassy, granular crystals are rounded and well-defined. This ferromagnesian silicate breaks with a conchoidal fracture, has a hardness of 6.5–7 and a specific gravity of 3.2–3.6.

Other classes of minerals, not represented here, are the sulfides—sulfur combined with a metal or a semi-metal; the phosphates—phosphorus and oxygen plus other elements; and the arsenates and vanadates—produced by substituting arsenic or vanadium for phosphorus. There are also the minerals composed of only one element. These include native metals (gold, iron and silver), non-metals (sulfur, diamond and graphite) and semi-metals (arsenic, bismuth and tellurium).

Chapter 4 / Rocks

The quantities, kinds and sizes of minerals contained in a rock—and the way in which the grains of these minerals are held together—determine a rock's appearance and physical properties. But rocks are not initially classified by mineral content. Instead, they are divided into three broad categories based on their mode of origin.

There are igneous rocks, formed by the solidification of cooling molten material. There are sedimentary rocks, formed from fragments of pre-existing rocks, or from chemical precipitates, or from organic deposits. And there are metamorphic rocks, formed by the alteration of igneous or sedimentary rocks at depth and under great heat and pressure.

CHARACTERISTICS OF IGNEOUS ROCKS

Underground molten rock is called magma, but if it reaches the surface through fissures and volcanic eruptions it is called lava. Cooled magma and lava form igneous rocks —the primary rocks of the earth.

Intrusive igneous rocks—also called plutonic rocks —are those that formed in deep underground chambers within the earth's crust. Extrusive igneous rocks—also called volcanic rocks—are those that formed at the surface of the earth.

All igneous rocks are classified in terms of their textures and mineral composition.

Texture The size, shape and pattern of a rock's mineral grains comprise its texture. The texture of an igneous rock usually indicates the conditions under which it cooled.

A fine-grained texture has crystals which cannot be seen by the naked eye. This is the texture of most volcanic rocks, which cool relatively fast because of exposure to the open air. Basalt, the widest-occurring volcanic rock, is an example.

A medium or coarse-grained texture has crystals large enough to be seen unaided. Most plutonic rocks, which cool slowly underground, have such a texture. Granite, the widest-occurring plutonic rock, is an example.

A glassy texture—which is essentially textureless and non-crystalline—results when the transformation from liquid to solid occurs too rapidly for crystals to form. Obsidian is an example.

A porphyritic or mixed texture refers to any igneous rock with crystals of two clearly different sizes. Such a texture indicates that the magma cooled in two stages— perhaps a slow-cooling phase followed by a period of more rapid cooling. In such rocks, the larger crystals are called phenocrysts and the background material in which they are imbedded is called the groundmass. The ground-mass may have a fine-grained, coarse-grained or glassy texture. Rhyolite is an example.

A pyroclastic or fragmented texture is produced by the reassembling of igneous rock shattered by volcanic explosions. It is composed of slivers of volcanic glass, bits of frothy pumice, phenocrysts and broken fragments of volcanic rock—all cemented or welded together. Volcanic tuff is an example.

Mineral Content The quantities and kinds of minerals in an igneous rock depend on the chemical content of the magma or lava from which it was formed.

Acidic rocks are high in silica. Quartz and feldspar predominate in them and they are light in color and low in specific gravity. Granite and rhyolite are examples.

Basic rocks have less silica, more iron and magnesium. Although some feldspar is frequently present, the ferro-magnesian minerals predominate—pyroxene, amphibole, olivine and biotite. These minerals make basic rocks darker and heavier than acidic rocks. Gabbro, dolerite and basalt are examples.

Because rocks grade from acidic to basic with no sharp distinctions from one to the next, there is a group between the extremes described as intermediate. Diorite is an example.

Ultrabasic rocks are like the basic rocks but have almost no feldspar. Dunite, peridotite and pyroxenite are examples.

COMMON IGNEOUS ROCKS

Granite The chief constituents of this coarse-grained acidic rock are quartz and feldspar, with some ferromagnesian minerals. Granite is generally white to light-gray, speckled with hornblende or black mica. But there is also an attractive red variety, displayed in the granite of Pikes Peak. Granite is the typical bedrock of the continents and constitutes the central core of many great mountain ranges.

(Note: Some granites are of metamorphic rather than of igneous origin.)

Rhyolite This volcanic rock has approximately the same chemical composition as the plutonic granite. But its texture is porphyritic, with a very fine-grained groundmass in which quartz, feldspar and, occasionally, biotite and ferromagnesian minerals are imbedded. Rhyolite is ordinarily

Granite is generally white to light gray, speckled with hornblende or black mica.

light—white, soft gray, pink. In the dry lands of south-western United States and northern Mexico, it is red. A characteristic of rhyolite's groundmass is a streaked pattern in the rock known as flow-banding.

(Note: Rhyolite is one of several fine-grained acidic and intermediate igneous rocks grouped together under the name of felsite.)

Obsidian Although most obsidian is black, it corresponds chemically to an average granite. Its textureless, glassy appearance—the result of super-fast cooling—frequently makes obsidian difficult to distinguish from manufactured glass. An example of this rock is Obsidian Cliff in Yellowstone National Park.

Pumice This light-gray to white rock, crowded with tiny bubbles, is a special kind of obsidian, petrified as a glassy froth because volcanic gases mixed into it before it solidified. Pumice is one of the lightest of rocks; its more porous varieties are able to float on water. It occurs widely in the western states.

Diorite This coarse-grained, drab-gray plutonic rock has an intermediate chemical composition—halfway between granite and gabbro. It contains plagioclase feldspar, but usually has no orthoclase and no quartz. Its most common ferromagnesian minerals are hornblende, biotite and, rarely, pyroxene. Diorite is found in the Sierra Nevadas of California.

When diorite contains quartz, it is known as quartz diorite. When diorite-like plutonic rocks contain orthoclase as well as plagioclase feldspar—with plagioclase dominant—they are called monzonites. A monzonite that also contains quartz is called a quartz monzonite and is very close to granite.

Andesite This fine-grained gray-to-gray-black rock is the volcanic equivalent of diorite in chemical composition. Phenocrysts are common—either as plagioclase crystals, transparent or light gray, or as dark minerals like hornblende or biotite. Andesite is abundant in volcano-capped mountain ranges such as the Cascades, the Carpathians and the Andes (for which it is named).

Obsidian, usually black as above, is textureless with a glassy appearance.

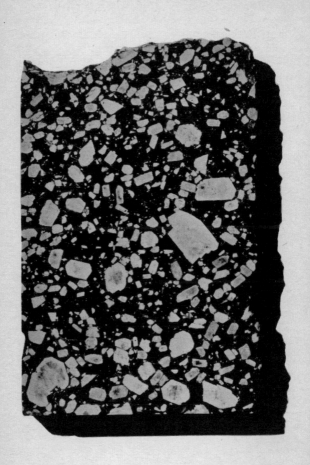

Porphyry is an igneous rock with at least 25% of its volume represented by phenocrysts.

Gabbro This coarse-grained plutonic basic rock is usually composed of plagioclase and pyroxene, with small amounts of other ferromagnesian minerals, particularly olivine. Pyroxene dominates and the rock is dark in color, although there are exceptions to this rule. Gabbro intermediate in grain size between regular gabbro ánd basalt is called dolerite or diabase. The Palisades of the Hudson River are dolerite.

Basalt This basic rock—black-to-gray, fine-grained, volcanic—is essentially plagioclase feldspar and pyroxene, chemically equivalent to gabbro. Most basalts are not porphyritic but some contain plagioclase and olivine phenocrysts. Basaltic lava flows form great plateaus in the northwestern United States, India and elsewhere, and are the chief constituents of many isolated oceanic islands.

Peridotite This is an ultrabasic plutonic rock consisting principally of olivine and pyroxene. When almost entirely olivine, the rock is dunite. When principally pyroxene, the rock is pyroxenite. A special variety of peridotite is kimberlite, a diamond-bearing rock found in South Africa and Arkansas.

Porphyry Any porphyritic-textured igneous rock with at least 25% of its volume represented by phenocrysts is a porphyry. Thus we can have diorite porphyry, andesite porphyry, etc.

Volcanic Tuff This is a fine-grained pyroclastic deposit composed of fragments under 4 mm in diameter.

Volcanic Breccia This rock is composed of fragments over 4 mm in diameter.

CHARACTERISTICS OF SEDIMENTARY ROCKS

By volume, sedimentary rocks are only about one-tenth as abundant as igneous rocks in the crust of the earth. Nevertheless, they cover about three-quarters of the earth's land surface.

Sediment may accumulate in a lake, a flood plain, a delta or the sea. Accumulations of sediment deposited by glaciers are present over great sections of North America and northern Europe. The Grand Canyon is an outstanding display of sedimentary rocks.

Three Categories   There are three categories of sedimentary rocks. Clastic rocks are fragments of pre-existing minerals, rock particles and shells carried to a site of deposition and cemented. Chemical precipitates—a second category—are accumulations of sediments, deposited when sea water, lakes or other solutions evaporate or are saturated. Organic sediments form a third category. All sedimentary rocks are, actually, mixtures of organic, chemical and clastic debris. The three categories, however, indicate their chief components and mode of formation.

The fragments that make up *clastic sedimentary rocks* are classified on the basis of size. A useful classification, proposed in 1922 by C. K. Wentworth and subsequently modified, is given below:

DIAMETER

FRAGMENT	mm	INCHES	NAME OF ROCK
Gravel			Conglomerate
Boulder	over 256	over 10	
Cobble	64–256	2.5–10	
Pebble	4–64	0.15–2.5	
Granule	2–4	0.07–0.15	
Sand (very fine			
to very coarse)	$1/16$–2	0.0025–0.07	Sandstone
Mud			Shale or Mudstone
Silt	$1/256$–$1/16$	0.00015–0.0025	
Clay	under $1/256$	under 0.00015	

NOTE: Quartz, a particularly hard and resistant mineral, generally remains in masses the size of gravel or sand. Feldspars and other silicates are softer than quartz and so are usually reduced to mud.

Chemical sedimentary rocks may occur when water containing dissolved solids evaporates. Most familiar of these evaporites, as they are called, is rock salt (halite), left when a saline lake or a mass of sea water cut off from the ocean dries up. Gypsum and anhydrite are other evaporites.

Other chemical sediments are limestone (which may also be clastic or organic), dolomite and certain siliceous rocks.

Organic sediments are composed of accumulations of the remains of plants and animals. Organically formed limestone represents the bulk of organic sediments.

Conversion into Rock Lithification—the conversion of loose sedimentary materials into solid rock—involves the processes of compaction and cementation. In compaction, water is squeezed out and the pressures of the overlying sediments push the materials closer together. Cementation involves the deposition of mineral matter between the grains, closing up the spaces that still separate them. Such substances as calcium carbonate, silica and iron oxide serve as effective natural cements, binding the grains into rock. Chemical sediments, unlike clastic rocks, have little or no cement. Instead, their grains are locked together by mutual interpenetration during growth.

Stratification Sedimentary rocks have, typically, a near-horizontal position unless altered by earth movements. The majority show distinct layers, or strata, an outstanding characteristic of these rocks.

Very thin layers are called laminae. The thicker layers are called beds. Different layers may show variations in texture, color or composition and may be the result of seasonal changes in rainfall, of storms, of fluctuations of sea level. If undisturbed, the youngest stratum is at the top and the oldest is at the bottom.

Color Sedimentary rocks are much more colorful than igneous rocks. Sometimes this color range is the result of the wide assortment of rocks from which the fragments come. Sometimes it is due to the cement that fills the space between the grains. Various forms of iron, for instance, may stain a rock red (as in the walls of the Grand Canyon), brown, pink, yellow, purple or green. Organic matter present in sedimentary rocks is another source of color, shading the rocks anywhere from light gray to black.

Special Markings Sedimentary rocks often preserve marks left on the surface of sediments by wind and water. These include corrugated ripple marks (parallel ridges made by moving air or water on mud or sand), craterlets (impressions made by raindrops) and mud cracked into polygonal figures (resulting from shrinkage of the ground in dry weather).

Fossils Fossils are a distinctive characteristic of sedimentary rocks, most commonly found in limestone, sandstone and shale. They are the remains of once-living plants and animals that died and were buried in sand, silt, lime or mud. Over the centuries, layer upon layer of sediment covered them, each pressing down on the one below. Dissolved minerals gradually replaced most parts of the organism, leaving permanent traces of teeth and bones and shells or the entire shape of an ancient plant or animal.

COMMON SEDIMENTARY ROCKS

Conglomerate Fragments of all sizes of gravel, with grains of sand and mud filling the spaces between, are cemented by mineral-laden water into the clastic sedimentary rock called conglomerate. Conglomerate is composed of rounded fragments, but a variety known as sedimentary breccia has fragments that are angular. Examples of this rock are the 2200-foot-thick Great Conglomerate, located in northern Michigan and Wisconsin, and the Great Smoky Conglomerate, exposed in the Great Smoky Mountains of Tennessee and North Carolina.

Sandstone Cemented sand grains, ranging in diameter from very fine ($\frac{1}{16}$ mm) to very coarse (2 mm), make up sandstone—one of the most varied of the clastic sedimentary rocks. Typical sand consists of quartz grains—rounded or sharp-edged, smooth and shiny or frosted, evenly sorted or quite unsorted by size. These grains are the chief components of quartz sandstone.

Two other important sandstones are arkose, common in the Connecticut Valley, and graywacke, named for the deposits in the Harz Mountains of Germany. Arkose has almost as much feldspar as quartz. Its color is usually red or pink, its grains somewhat angular. Arkoses are generally formed by rapid erosion and deposition of coarse feldspar-

Conglomerate is composed of fragments
of different sizes of gravel, with grains of
sand and mud filling the spaces between.

rich rocks like granite, with little abrasion or rounding of
individual grains. Graywacke contains many rock fragments, in addition to its quartz and feldspar minerals. It is
commonly gray, dark green or black. The angular graywacke grains also show signs of rapid erosion, rapid deposition and little weathering.

Shale   This fine-grained clastic is the most abundant of
all sedimentary rocks. Although it appears homogeneous
to the naked eye, it is actually made up of minute clay
flakes and silt particles, with tiny mineral fragments of
quartz, feldspar and mica. Shale may be found in its dark
variety throughout the Appalachian region. But shales
are also dark gray, green or purple-red. This rock is usually
fissile—able to split along well-developed and closely
spaced planes.

Halite (Rock Salt)   Many different salts are chemically
precipitated when sea water evaporates, but this one-
mineral rock is the most abundant. Thick beds of rock

salt, accompanied by gypsum and anhydrite, are found in many areas, among them Texas, New Mexico, Germany, Iran and India. Beds of salt are often colored brown or red by iron oxide. Gypsum beds may be white, pink, gray or a dark color.

Gypsum and Anhydrite Both these chemical precipitates will separate out early in the process of evaporation of sea water, accumulating in quantity from water not saline enough to precipitate halite. Gypsum and anhydrite are one-mineral rocks—anhydrite changing to gypsum in the presence of moisture, the reverse occurring when gypsum loses water.

Limestone This rock is predominantly composed of the mineral calcite ($CaCO_3$), but impurities—SiO_2 or $MgCO_3$ —may be present.

Clastic limestones are composed of broken and worn fragments of shells or crystals of calcite. In many respects they are comparable to sandstone, except that the grains are small pieces of fossil shells or fragments of coral rather than quartz or feldspar. The sands of the Florida Keys are made up of worn calcite grains.

Chemically precipitated limestone is often difficult to distinguish from that of organic origin. However, the very fine-grained, white, flour-like, calcareous ooze found in the Great Bahama Banks is most likely a direct chemical precipitate from the shallow sea water covering this shoal.

A soft limestone deposited from spring water saturated with calcium carbonate is called travertine. It is coarsely crystalline, full of small irregular holes and colored pale yellow or cream if pure, brown or darker yellow if not. Distinctive bandings in complex, curving patterns are often present.

Fresh-water limestone laid down in the beds of lakes is sometimes called marl.

Organic limestone is more abundant than chemically precipitated limestone. It is also the most abundant organic sedimentary rock. It is built of limy shells and skeletons, which are in turn built of calcium carbonate extracted by living organisms from the water in which they live.

Some organic limestones are coral reefs, such as

Organic limestone is composed of limy shells and skeletons which were built of calcium carbonate.

Australia's Great Barrier Reef, which contains many organisms besides coral. Others are algal limestones, thick layers of which are found in Texas, composed of calcite precipitated by algae and bacteria. Still another form is coquina, made up of mollusk and gastropod shells. A limestone composed of the remains of tiny, single-celled, free-floating animals called foraminifera is chalk—dramatically exhibited in the White Cliffs of Dover.

Dolomite This one-mineral rock looks like, accompanies and grades into limestone. But limestone will fizz if acid is spilled on it, while dolomite will not. Most dolomite is probably limestone altered by magnesium-bearing solutions.

Fine-Grained Siliceous Rocks These may be chemically precipitated or of organic origin. The most common silica-rich rock is chert—which includes dark varieties called flint. Petrified wood is another fine-grained siliceous rock —formed by the replacement of wood by silica-bearing solutions.

Coal This organic rock is derived from plant life which began as lush vegetation in dark swamp forests. As these plants died and fell into the swamp, they were buried by sediments that protected them from complete destruction. An increase in pressure expelled moisture and gas, the carbon in the plants became concentrated and the deposits passed successively from peat to lignite to bituminous to anthracite and, in some cases, to graphite or pure carbon. (Anthracite and graphite are generally considered metamorphic rocks.)

CHARACTERISTICS OF METAMORPHIC ROCKS

The third major category of rock types has neither the textures and mineral compositions typical of igneous rocks, nor the stratification, fossils and other features sedimentary rocks display. These are the metamorphic rocks, produced by the transformation of igneous and sedimentary rocks, while in a solid state deep within the crust of the earth, through heat, pressure and chemical activity. Alteration may be partial, leaving clear traces of a rock's former origin, but usually alteration is complete.

A rock's texture may be altered through the process of recrystallization—the enlargement of the original crystals resulting in a more coarsely crystalline rock. A rock's chemical composition may be altered too, through the formation of new minerals.

These new minerals, or the elongation, flattening or reorientation of the original crystals, may further change the rock by producing a structure called foliation. Foliated rocks are banded or layered, due to a parallel arrangement of their minerals, and for the most part will split readily along the foliations.

There are several different processes of metamorphism. In contact metamorphism, heat plays the dominant role, while the chemical activity of fluids and gases is more important in hydrothermal metamorphism. Crustal folding at relatively shallow depths produces dynamic metamorphism. In regional or dynamothermal metamorphism, directed heat and pressure work together. Plutonic metamorphism involves great depths, very high temperatures and great pressure. The pressure in plutonic metamorphism is hydrostatic (equal in all directions) rather than directed (greater in one direction, less in another).

COMMON METAMORPHIC ROCKS

Among the most common of the metamorphic rocks are slate, schist, gneiss, marble and quartzite. The first three are foliated, the last two nonfoliated.

Slate   This is an abundant, very fine-grained, well-foliated rock that splits readily into thin sheets along parallel, smooth, closely spaced surfaces. (Such a property is called rock cleavage, as distinct from the mineral cleavage discussed earlier.) Most slate is derived from the metamorphism of shale, and shows remnants of such sedimentary features as stratification, pebbles and fossils. In the process of recrystallization the shale clay flakes become mica.

Slate is usually dark-gray, but may also be green, purple, red, yellow, brown or mottled. It occurs in the Appalachian states—Pennsylvania, Vermont, Maine and Georgia—where ancient sediments were compressed into mountains.

Mica schist is one variety of the widely occurring metamorphic rock, schist.

Marble, most lovely of the rocks, ranges from the tiny-grained to the coarsely crystalline, from pure white to markings of many hues.

Schist This is believed to be the most widely occurring metamorphic rock, made from a great range of rocks, including muddy sandstone, clayey limestone and basalt. Chlorite schist (also called greenschist) is soft, greasy, fine-grained, green in color. In mica schist, muscovite or quartz or biotite predominates. Amphibole schist is composed chiefly of amphibole and plagioclase. A big belt of schist, accompanied by gneiss, runs from Washington to New York.

Gneiss This abundant, coarse-grained rock, pronounced *nice,* has the general composition of granite and shows a distinctly banded structure. Each layer contains a different mineral, and frequently light and dark mineral bands alternate. Feldspar is quite commonly found in this rock; so are quartz, amphibole, garnet and mica.

Gneisses are metamorphosed from many different

rocks, including granite, shale, rhyolite, diorite, slate and schist. Despite their uniform banding, gneisses do not have the good rock cleavage of slate and schist.

Marble Most lovely of the rocks, marble is produced by the metamorphism of limestone or dolomite. This stone ranges from tiny-grained to coarsely crystalline, from pure white to markings of many hues—black, gray, yellow brown, red and green. Carrara marble is found in Italy, Pentelic marble in Greece and Yule marble in Colorado.

Quartzite This is a glistening, very hard, sugar-textured rock, chiefly composed of interlocking quartz grains. Its typical coloring is light (white, pink, pale gray or red) but it may also be brown or black. This rock is formed by the metamorphism of quartz sandstone, but unlike most sandstones it breaks across the grains, not around them. It is displayed in the Nelson Range, also called the Quartzite Range, of British Columbia.

THE REMAKING OF ROCKS

The transition from igneous to sedimentary to metamorphic rock is not uncommon. Even the deepest granite, frozen from molten material far within the earth's crust, may ultimately be exposed. Split, torn, crushed, blown or washed away, fragments of the rock may then be deposited in layers, which build one upon the other and finally consolidate into a solid mass. This sedimentary rock will, in turn, be metamorphosed if buried deeply and subjected to drastic changes in its geologic environment. And, under certain circumstances, the metamorphic rock may be re-melted, to return again to its original igneous state.

Chapter 5 / Weathering, Soils and Gravity

Rocks exposed at the surface of the earth must ultimately disintegrate and decompose through a process known as weathering. Weathering is responsible for wiping away the epitaphs from tombstones, the exquisite hieroglyphs from obelisks, the paint from houses. It is also responsible for breaking up the earth's solid bedrock into a mantle of loose fragments known as the regolith, from which is formed that most precious of all mineral resources—soil.

Rocks may disintegrate—break up mechanically— with no change except a reduction of the parent rock mass into smaller pieces. But they may also decompose—break up chemically—changing into new substances with different physical properties and chemical compositions. Chemical weathering is far more extensive, more rapid and more complete than mechanical weathering.

MECHANICAL WEATHERING

Reduced Pressure As natural agencies wear away rocks, those that lie beneath may develop crevices and seams of weakness as a result of reduced pressure. These cracks, which permit water, roots and organic acid-bearing solutions to enter, are of great importance in weathering. Almost all rocks display cracks, called joints. Sometimes the joints are closely spaced; sometimes, as in the cliff of El Capitan in Yosemite Valley, they are dozens of feet apart.

Temperature Changes It was once believed that exfoliation—the scaling off of a rock around its surface to produce an onion-layered appearance—was the product of

The cliff of El Capitan in Yosemite Valley displays cracks (joints), dozens of feet apart.

its alternate expansion and contraction induced by severe temperature changes. It was reasoned that a rock in the desert, for instance, became heated (thus expanding) during the burning day and cooled drastically (thus contracting) when temperatures dropped sharply at night. Since rock is a poor conductor of heat, the theory continued, only its outer layers were significantly affected. The strains set up by this alternate heating and cooling, it was asserted, were responsible for exfoliation.

Such a theory, however, could not explain why the 4000-year-old monuments of the Sahara Desert have remained virtually undisturbed over the centuries. Experimenters were also baffled by the fact that granite, subjected in the laboratory to the equivalent of 1000 years of extreme temperature shifts, insistently maintained a bright polish and uncracked surface.

Obviously, temperature changes alone could not cause rocks to scale off. While they remain a minor factor in weathering, experiments have determined that the crucial element in the exfoliation process is water.

When water—even the sporadic rain or nocturnal

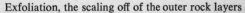

Exfoliation, the scaling off of the outer rock layers

dew of the arid desert—enters into chemical combination with minerals of certain rocks, the rocks will swell. It is this incorporation of water, rather than temperature changes themselves, that provides the shove needed to drop off the outer rock layers in concentric shells. Thus a chemical change (an increase in volume through hydration) helps to produce a mechanical result (exfoliation).

Half Dome, in Yosemite National Park, is an example of exfoliated rock.

Freezing and Thawing When water freezes, it expands about 9%. If confined, frozen water delivers a powerful outward thrust of at least 288,000 pounds per square foot.

Water entering cracks in rocks will pry them apart if trapped there and changed to ice. This process, called frost wedging, is of primary importance in mechanical weathering.

The best conditions for frost wedging are not in the Arctic, where everything remains frozen throughout the winter, but in high mountainous regions, where there is thawing by day and freezing by night. Each day water

in concentric shells, can be seen in the Sierras.

from melting snow enters the cracks; each night the water freezes, expands and opens the crack a little more, until the rock is shattered.

When water contained in the pores of soil freezes and expands, the result is frost heaving, which causes roads to buckle and thrusts boulders to the surface of farmland.

In polar regions a zone of perennially frozen ground has survived since the Ice Age because of low mean temperature. It underlies about 20% of the earth's land surface, including 80% of Alaska and about 50% of Canada.

Organic Agents Living organisms help reduce rock to soil, and mix the soil with great effectiveness. One example of mechanical weathering through organic agents is the splitting of rocks by growing plant roots, which may stubbornly force their way into rock crevices when there is no soil in which to take hold. Burrowing animals—earthworms, ants and termites—are responsible for the excavation of great quantities of soil.

CHEMICAL WEATHERING

Although mechanical and chemical weathering are each discussed separately here, they rarely operate independently in nature. Through mechanical weathering, new rock surfaces are exposed. Then water, oxygen and carbon dioxide react chemically with the minerals of the rock, slowly decomposing them into new minerals.

Solution Water serves as a solvent for many of the minerals in rocks. The process whereby water dissolves mineral and rock material is known as leaching. The presence of carbon dioxide increases water's solvent powers immensely. Carbon dioxide, supplied by the air and by decaying organic matter in the soil, forms carbonic acid when dissolved in water. A simple example of chemical weathering by solution is the combination of limestone (calcium carbonate) with carbonic acid to form the soluble compound calcium bicarbonate.

Hydration Chemical combination with water to produce a new compound is known as hydration. One result of this process, as noted in the discussion of exfoliation, is a large increase in the volume of a rock. Hydration also results in less dense and less cohesive materials, altering firm feldspar to soft clay—a common soil substance.

Oxidation   Oxygen is the chief constituent provided by the atmosphere for chemical reaction with rocks and soils. Iron compounds, especially pyrite, are particularly affected by this gas. The addition of oxygen (oxidation) to iron-rich rocks alters their color by rusting them to reds, yellows and oranges. Thus the gray-green ferrous iron oxide, when chemically combined with oxygen, yields the rust-colored ferric iron oxide. Oxidation also releases corrosive acids, which help to decompose rock.

Carbonation   Carbon dioxide is one of the principal agents of chemical weathering. It not only increases the solvent power of water as described above: it also combines with many different minerals to form compounds (carbonates) which may be very soluble. Silicates, for example, are extremely resistant to solvent action. When changed into carbonates, however, they can be removed in solution.

Organic Agents   An important part of chemical weathering is the release of carbon dioxide through the respiration of plants and animals and through the decay of organic materials in the soil. Decayed vegetable matter, or humus, also helps make humic acid which, like other acids, speeds up the decomposition of rocks.

CONDITIONS OF WEATHERING

Some rocks will last longer than others, but sooner or later even the most resistant rock will be weathered away. Climate and the nature of the rock involved are the principal factors in determining the speed and way in which a rock weathers.

Sometimes weathering will occur at different rates in the same rock if some of its portions are less compact, more soluble or softer than other parts. Differential weathering, as this process is called, removes the weaker sections first, leaving the stronger areas of rock standing out in sharp relief. Differential weathering produces grooving, carving, pitting or fretting in a rock. It is also responsible for the grotesque shapes of "balanced" and "pedestal" or "mushroom" rocks.

In cold or dry climates (polar regions, high mountains, deserts), the weathering is essentially mechanical, with frost action an important force in the breaking up of rocks. Chemical weathering is dominant in hot, humid areas with abundant vegetation and a large supply of organic acids—powerful agents of rock decay.

A rock may deteriorate in one locale and decompose in another, yielding quite different products in each case. The weathering of granite, for instance, is very different in a warm, rainy climate—where it yields rust-stained sandy clay—from what it is in the dryness of the desert—where it disintegrates into separate sand grains.

Gravestones and obelisks provide useful information about the weathering of different rocks in the same climate, and of the same rocks in different climates.

In New England, slate gravestones of the 1700's still retain their inscriptions while epitaphs traced on more recent markers of marble or limestone have already been obliterated.

A classic testimonial to the diversity of weathering is the hieroglyph-bedecked Egyptian obelisks. Those standing in the placid heat of the desert have remained almost unchanged after 4000 years. But transported to the steamy summers, sleety winters and exhaust-fume-laden air of New York City, an obelisk of the same period began coming apart in less than a century.

SOILS

Soil is disintegrated and decomposed bedrock to which have been added the products of decaying matter, called humus. Soil can also be described as that part of the regolith capable of supporting plant life. Although rocks contain the elements necessary to sustain plant growth, these are generally unavailable to plants until the rocks are broken down.

As weathering progresses, the constituents of primitive soil become finer and finer. For a while soil retains the characteristics of its parent rock, and is described as immature. But eventually the soil loses all resemblance to the rock from which it was developed. At that point it is said to be mature.

A mature soil consists of three layers, or horizons, which together form a complete soil profile.

In the A horizon (also called topsoil, or the eluvial zone) the soluble constituents are very largely leached out. Organic matter is added, however, making this zone of soil quite black and humus-laden in some climates.

Some of the materials washed out of the A horizon are carried down to the B horizon (or subsoil, or illuvial zone), where they may accumulate. Iron oxide, particularly, collects in this zone, sometimes forming a cemented, unyielding "hardpan." In arid regions, a limy encrustation called calliche may build up in the subsoil.

The C horizon is a transitional zone. Its upper regions are true soil, its lower regions rock fragments blending into bedrock.

Variations in soil profiles are produced chiefly by differences in climate, with differences in parent rock becoming increasingly unimportant as the soil matures. In the long run, soils derived from sandstone, granite and basalt may appear almost identical if formed under identical climatic conditions.

Three distinct climates produce these three major soil groups:

Chernozems (or mollisols) are highly fertile soils, among the most productive in the world. They form in semi-arid regions, like the Russian steppes and the western plains of the United States and Canada, under a generous vegetation of native grasses. The A horizon of chernozems is always a rich black, colored by the abundant organic matter supplied by the partly decomposed grass roots.

Podzols (or spodosols) develop in the cool, humid regions of the world, particularly in coniferous and hardwood deciduous forests. The A horizon is leached out white or gray, while the brown or gray-brown B horizon is characterized by an accumulation of organic material, iron and aluminum washed down from above. There is sometimes enough iron dissolved out of the upper layer to form a hardpan. Podzols are more thoroughly leached out than chernozems and thus these soils are less fertile.

Laterites (or oxisols) are red-brown soils which develop best in well-drained tropics (India, Nigeria, Brazil) with clearly defined wet and dry seasons. Laterites are enduring building materials because they are composed chiefly of iron and aluminum oxide, all the other minerals having been weathered away. For the same reason, however, these soils are very unsatisfactory for agriculture.

GRAVITY

One major result of weathering, as we have just learned, is the creation of soil. Another important result is the preparation of rocks for their eventual removal by agents of erosion.

Although weathering refers, technically, to the in-place disintegration and decomposition of rock, while erosion involves rock removal, it is difficult in practical terms to separate the two. In nature, weathering and

erosion operate hand in hand to break down the solid rock and carry it away—ultimately to the sea.

The transportation of rock fragments from higher to lower elevations is handled by many agents of erosion. When gravity itself is the determining agent, the transportation process is called mass movement. Mass movement may be violently swift, imperceptibly slow, or any velocity in between.

Creep The slowest and most widespread of downslope movements, producing considerable changes over long periods of time, goes by the undistinguished name of creep. Unless a land surface is utterly flat, soil is bound to gravitate or "creep" slowly downhill. Creep typically occurs in unconsolidated materials on grass-covered slopes.

Any disturbance of soil is likely to leave soil grains in a lower position than before. Thus creep may be caused by the enlargement of growing roots, the activities of sheep,

A mudflow is a streaming mass of mud and water moving down the floor of a stream channel, often burdened by boulders.

cattle or burrowing animals, the expansion and contraction of soil constituents, or even, to a very slight extent, the gravitational pull of the sun and moon (which raises tides in solid rock and is capable of disturbing rock particles).

Decayed boulders, once rounded, are stretched into long thin ribbons of varicolored soil by creep. Creep also dislodges blocks from their outcrops, displaces fences, walls and gravestones, and cracks sidewalks and retaining walls.

Solifluction   When water enters the pores of soil, it adds weight to the weathered material. It also serves as a lubricant, allowing soil grains to slide readily. The result is a slow downhill flow of water-saturated soil, called solifluction.

Solifluction is most common in permafrost areas, where the surface layer of soil thaws in the summer but cannot lose its water to the hard-frozen ground below. Heavily laden with water, the soil sluggishly travels down even the most moderate slopes and along the floors of steep valleys in sheets, lobes and tongues, producing a landscape that resembles, as one geologist colorfully described it, "the wrinkled hide of an aged elephant."

Earthflow   This is a faster earth movement than creep or solifluction. Characteristic of grass-covered hills with a blanket of soil, earthflow is most likely to occur when the ground is saturated with water.

Mudflow   Similar to an earthflow but faster moving, a mudflow is a streaming mass of mud and water moving down the floor of a stream channel, often with a burden of boulders and rocks. A mudflow may be powerful enough to sweep up trucks and bury houses lying in its path.

In arid and semi-arid regions, a sudden cloudburst will fill up empty stream courses with a torrent of chocolate mudflow.

In alpine regions, mudflows occur when great quantities of water released by melting snow mingle with loose rock debris and tumble down steep slopes. A mudflow of this type rolled down a Norwegian valley one night in 1893, taking 111 lives.

Still another kind of mudflow is caused by active volcanoes. A destructive volcano-produced mudflow occurred in 1919, when Gunong Keloet erupted on a lake floor in Indonesia. The overflowing waters mixed with volcanic debris and swept down the slopes, choking 104 villages and killing more than 5000 people.

Talus and Rock Glacier   When weathering occurs on cliffs or hillsides, particles of rock—ranging in size from a fraction of an inch to several feet in diameter—slide or fall to lower positions. These particles are called talus. Talus refers both to the fallen rock fragments at the foot of the cliff and to the entire accumulated mass, which sometimes piles up back to the cliff's crest to form a talus slope.

Rock glaciers are masses of coarse talus materials which slowly travel down mountain slopes as a ponderous lobe with a wrinkled surface and steep sides. If their course is over a cliff, rock glaciers may form spectacular rock "cascades."

Landslide   This is the dropping of great masses of material at a velocity approximating free fall.

Landslides most commonly occur when large amounts of weathered material, accumulated on a steep slope, are set into motion by the increased weight and lubrication of water from rains or melting snow. But sometimes landslides involve solid bedrock, which crashes downward when unsettled by an earthquake, or by cracks in the rock, or by the disrupting construction activities of man.

A catastrophic landslide occurred in the town of Frank, Alberta, in 1903, when a mass of limestone blocks broke loose from the crest of Turtle Mountain. The deadly debris—40 million cubic yards of rock—plunged down the steep slope, roared two miles across the valley and then, swept upward by its momentum, climbed 400 feet onto the slope at the opposite side. This landslide left 70 people dead.

All these movements of rock and soil are the result of the direct action of gravity. But, as future chapters will show, gravity also works in concert with streams, ground water, glaciers, wind and waves. Its most important role, in fact, is a secondary one—to supply these agents of long-distance erosion with the weathered fragments of the earth.

Chapter 6 / The Work of Flowing Streams

A stream is a body of water flowing in a channel. It may be swift or sluggish, muddy or clear, a quiet brook, a tumbling creek or a great river. Taken together, flowing streams are the most important geologic force operating on the surface of the earth, capable of moving colossal amounts of sediment from place to place. Much of the natural architecture that diversifies the land has been built by running water making its way to the sea.

FROM RAINDROP TO RIVER SYSTEM

Run-off Day after day, century after century, water evaporates from the surface of the earth and returns as rain or snow. Some of this precipitated water promptly evaporates into the atmosphere again. Some sinks into the ground and becomes ground water. Another portion is temporarily locked up in snow fields and glaciers. About a third of the water that falls on the land travels to the sea via surface channels, and is known as run-off.

Run-off includes not only the precipitation that flows into streams during and following rains, but ground water that subsequently makes its way into streams from springs and seepages.

A large proportion of the total run-off is carried by a handful of the world's largest rivers. The Amazon, 4000 miles long, drains a land area of 2,722,000 square miles. The other rivers include the Congo (3000 miles long, drains 1,425,000 square miles); the Mississippi-Missouri (4200 miles long, drains 1,240,000 square miles); Rio de la Plata (2300 miles long, drains 1,198,000 square miles); the Nile (3473 miles long, drains 1,107,000 square miles); and the Yangtze (3000 miles long, drains 650,000 square miles).

Sheet Erosion An average 15 million tons of water drop upon the earth every second. During a single shower, more than a billion tons may fall. Before this rain is channeled in streams, it has an important erosional effect on loose, soft or extensively weathered material. As thin films or sheets of rain water run off slopes, they dislodge particles of soil and sweep them to lower levels. Unless a vulnerable area is forested, or covered with earth-hugging vegetation or contour-plowed, it will eventually be rendered agriculturally worthless due to the loss of its rich topsoil, valuable minerals and organic constituents.

Birth of a Stream A stream is born when a flowing sheet of rain water breaks up into rivulets, occupies small gullies in the land and begins swiftly to enlarge them. Each channel is deepened and widened, and lengthened toward the mouth of the stream (its lower end) and toward its head (its source, or point of origin).

Types of Streams A stream may be permanent (perennial), flowing throughout the year, because it traverses a zone where the water table intersects its channel (see Chapter 7). It may be temporary (intermittent), carrying water only part of the time because it is heavily dependent on melting snow or precipitation. It may even be ephemeral, existing for a brief spell only when a heavy rainfall occurs.

Course of Streams If the course of a stream is determined simply by the slope and shape of the land, it is called a consequent stream. If, in the process of its development, the stream alters its course, taking routes which follow the softer underlying rocks and avoiding the harder rocks when possible, it is known as a subsequent stream.

Tributaries As a stream develops, tributaries grow and branch out from the main course. Typically, the tributaries are arranged like the limbs of a tree and are said to have a dendritic pattern. But sometimes they display a rectangular, or trellis, pattern. And sometimes tributaries radiate from a high central zone and show a radial pattern.

Some tributaries are stronger than others, because of a larger quantity of water, a softer bed, a swifter flow. A stronger stream may undercut the divide separating it from the weaker, thereby capturing and diverting its water. This process is called stream piracy, and the stream which has lost its headwaters is said to have been beheaded. The Canadian River in Edmond, Oklahoma, is presently threatened with beheading by one of its tributaries.

River System From its beginning as a tiny rivulet, a flowing stream may become part of a complex river system. The system consists of a main valley and all its tributaries and subtributaries. A river valley is the valley which has been excavated, to any extent, by the stream which occupies it. The trough in the bottom of the valley in which the water flows is called the channel. A river's drainage basin (or watershed) is the entire land area drained by the river and its tributaries.

CHARACTERISTICS OF STREAMS

Types of Flow The water in streams moves in two distinct ways—by laminar flow and by turbulent flow. Laminar flow is streamlined and orderly; the water particles glide past each other on parallel paths, never criss-crossing or intermingling. Turbulent flow is by far the more significant stream motion. As its name implies, it shows no precise pattern but is quite irregular. Although the water travels, essentially, forward, there are all sorts of random swirling and eddying movements. The white water at the bottom of the Grand Coulee Dam's spillway is an outstanding example of turbulent flow.

Gradient A stream requires only a very slight inclination of its bed in order to keep moving. The Amazon, for instance, falls only $\frac{1}{5}$ inch per mile. The measure of the slope down which a stream flows is called its gradient. A stream's longitudinal profile is a graphic outline of its gradient over long portions of its course.

Velocity Gradient is just one of several factors that determine a stream's velocity, which rarely exceeds 10 miles an hour and more usually tends to be under 5. Swift streams are those that have a high gradient, a large volume of water, a straight and narrow channel and a relatively small load of material.

Discharge   This is the quantity of water passing a given point on the stream bank in a given interval of time, measured in cubic feet per second. The discharge of most streams is inconstant, showing dramatic increases during times of heavy rainfall or rapidly melting snow, and decreasing dramatically in times of drought.

Stream Load   The material carried by a stream from its point of erosion to its place of deposition is called the stream load. This load is drawn from loose, weathered rock brought into flowing water by rain, wind, melting glaciers or mass movement. Dissolved solids from rocks and soil also pour into the stream. Still another source of stream load is the material obtained from the bottom and sides of the channel itself.

Running water removes material from its bed in a number of ways. Direct hydraulic action—the force of the water itself—is one method of removal, not very significant unless the rock is weak or the current is strong. Solvent action works on such bed materials as limestone and gypsum, and dissolves the cementing materials of other rocks. Streams also loosen and pick up particles when there are cracks in the bed, or an arrangement of rocks in thin layers. This form of erosion, known as quarrying, produces most of the boulders and pebbles that roll or bounce along the bottom of streams. These materials, as well as sand, play a crucial role in stream-bed erosion by grinding and scouring the bottom and sides of channels.

As the load is carried along, the running water reduces or obliterates projections, creating a rounded effect. Sometimes a sharp rock will show rounding after a journey of only a mile. The longer the trip, of course, the more perfect the rounding, except in the case of tiny silt grains or fine sand.

Competence   The maximum size particle that a stream is capable of carrying under a given set of conditions is called its competence. Competence depends primarily on velocity, but there is far more than a one-to-one correlation between the two. When the velocity of a stream is doubled, it can move a rock 64 times bigger than the one it could move before the increase!

Many geologists' favorite example of the fantastic

The Rio Grande River flows
through a canyon in Big Bend
National Park, Texas.

moving power of streams is the collapse of the 205-foot San Francisquito Dam in California in 1928. A wave of water 125 feet high swept down the canyon at a velocity of about 50 miles per hour, carrying blocks of concrete weighing some 10,000 tons half a mile downstream.

Capacity The total load that a stream is capable of carrying under a given set of conditions is called its capacity. Capacity depends not only on velocity but on discharge. A tiny stream flowing at the same velocity as the Mississippi, for instance, cannot possibly move an equivalent load.

Grade A graded stream has achieved a gradient (slope) that enables it to maintain a just-right balance between velocity, size, amount of load, etc. Such a gradient would display, ideally, a concave-upward curve, nearly horizontal at the mouth and steeper near the head.

A stream whose load is equal to its capacity is said to be at grade. A stream whose capacity is greater than its load will pick up additional material. A stream whose load is greater than its capacity will get rid of its burden. Thus an underloaded stream, which has a large amount of energy, is an effective agent of erosion, while an overloaded stream, which has a small amount of energy, is an agent of deposition.

STREAM EROSION

Stream erosion involves not only the carving of a stream's narrow channel, but the lowering of the areas between streams as well. Weathering and mass movement downslope are critically involved in this wide-range landscape reduction, with the stream ceaselessly cutting and carrying off rock until a broad and nearly level upland is worn to a broad and nearly featureless plain.

The lowest level to which a drainage system can erode a land surface—ultimately sea level—is known as the base level of erosion. The eroded, low-lying surface itself is called a peneplain, which is an "almost-plain" interrupted only by isolated, rounded rock masses called monadnocks. In the course of lowering the land to this point, however, running water creates canyons, falls, rapids and many other dramatic topographic effects.

Canyons While some valleys are the result of the position of the underlying bedrock, most have been formed by stream erosion. When stream erosion proceeds more rapidly than rock weathering, the river valley will be cut quite deep relative to its width and may become a canyon with V-shaped walls.

Canyons develop best in locales of high elevation and aridity. Here running water shoots down high gradients with great erosive power while mechanical weathering works slowly on the rocks, leaving banks firm and steep-sided.

Thus, many imposing canyons are found in the mountain plateau regions of the American West. There is the symmetrical 1000-foot-deep canyon of the Yellowstone

The ruggedly beautiful Grand Canyon was carved out over the

River, its banks displaying the colorful rocks that have earned the region its name. There are the Royal Gorge of the Arkansas, the Black Canyon of the Gunnison, the Flaming Gorge of the Green River, the gorge of the Shoshone, the canyons of the Wind River, Big Horn and Snake —all streams flowing out of the Rockies. And there is the ruggedly beautiful Grand Canyon—king of them all— carved over the course of many million years by the powerful Colorado River. This great gash in the earth's crust measures about 200 miles long, up to 16 miles wide and, in places, over a mile deep.

Falls and Rapids Between its head waters and its mouth, a stream may show great irregularities in gradient. A rapid is a noticeable increase in gradient; a fall is steeper. Small falls, which often occur in series, are called cascades.

Most falls are the result of unequal erosion by the

course of many millions of years
by the powerful Colorado River.

stream itself. Sometimes this is caused by the passing of streams from soft rocks—which they readily erode—to harder rocks—which give way far more slowly. The falls and rapids of the Potomac River in Washington, D.C., are produced in this way, the river forming rapids at the boundary (fall line) between the harder rocks of the Piedmont area of the Appalachians and the softer rocks of the Coastal Plain.

A very favorable condition for the formation of falls or rapids is the presence of hard strata overlying or alternating with soft strata. The spectacular Niagara Falls, for instance, drops from an 80-foot limestone ledge which overlies softer shales and thin-bedded limestones. Every minute a load of 93 million gallons of water takes the 150-foot drop, implacably washing away the weaker rock under the falls. Gradually the tough limestone brim is undermined, and now and then chunks of it drop off. As a result, Niagara Falls retreats steadily upstream. At the same time it becomes lower, because the stratum forming the brim dips slightly upstream.

Falls are also produced by unequal erosion that occurs when hard igneous rocks lie between soft sedimentaries. Examples are Upper Yellowstone Falls, which drops 110 feet, and Lower Yellowstone Falls, which drops 310.

When a main channel has been eroded more rapidly than a tributary, there is a drop at their junction point down which water may plunge. Falls of this type are found in Yosemite Valley.

As the waters drop over a fall, they cut a plunge pool in the stream bed below. In the Grand Coulee, an abandoned channel of the Columbia River, there is a plunge pool 80 feet deep and ½ mile wide, formed when the river fell over a 400-foot cliff.

Potholes Although smaller, potholes are similar to the plunge pools cut by waterfalls. These cavities, however, are carved into the bedrock of streams by the abrasive action of swirling sand- and gravel-laden water. Potholes, also called giants' caldrons or kettles, are roughly circular and range in size from just a few feet across to a diameter of several yards. In New Hampshire, the Pemigewasset

When a main channel has been eroded more rapidly than a tributary, there is a drop at their junction point down which water may plunge. Yosemite Falls.

River has hollowed out an impressive 20-foot-diameter pothole called the Basin.

Structural Terraces and Cliffs   These structures often line the sides of valleys and canyons. They come about when streams cut through horizontal layers of differing hardness, causing the eroded edge of each resistant bed to form a cliff, and the top of the bed to form a step or structural terrace. The Grand Canyon displays both cliffs and terraces.

Utah's famous Rainbow Bridge has a span of 278 feet and an arch 309 feet high.

Natural Bridges Most natural bridges are formed when a stream flowing over a limestone or sandstone bed seeps into cracks in the underlying rock and cuts out an underground channel. Eventually all the stream water is diverted underground, where erosion continues until part of the original stream bed becomes a bridge spanning the stream.

Sometimes two potholes, bigger on the bottom than on top, will enlarge and unite underground, leaving the narrow top strip between to bridge the cavity.

Still other natural bridges are formed when a stream undercuts a narrow divide between parallel canyons, or grinds an opening through an obstruction in its channels. This last method created Utah's famous Rainbow Bridge, with a span of 278 feet and an arch 309 feet high.

Monuments, Mesas and Buttes   As steam erosion assaults an elevated landmass in a semi-arid climate, isolated structures, sometimes grotesque, sometimes awe-inspiring, rise above the less resistant material of the surrounding, lowering region. Among these are monuments, mesas and buttes.

Monuments are tall and narrow shafts, towers and pillars. Mesas are flat-topped, horizontal structures, bounded on all sides by steep cliffs and capped by a hard layer. The undercutting of this layer causes mesas to shrink in area as they grow in height relative to the rest of the region. Still flat-topped, but now vertical, these isolated erosional remains are known as buttes. The vividly colored horizontal rocks of the Colorado plateau form handsome mesas, buttes and monuments.

Cuestas and Hogbacks   Other by-products of erosion in the reduction of semi-arid lands are cuestas and hogbacks. Cuestas are asymmetric ridges, sloping steeply on one side, gently on another, and capped with resistant rock. They can be seen in Arizona, New Mexico and along the Atlantic and Gulf Coasts. Hogbacks, more steeply dipping ridges, appear around the bases of the Rockies in Colorado.

STREAM TRANSPORTATION

There are three principal ways in which a stream transports its load.

Soluble materials, such as calcium carbonate and various salts, are carried in solution. This invisible dissolved load gives some streams their distinctive taste. The loss of soluble chemicals is so great that the lands of the world will be lowered, by solution alone, about 1 foot in 30,000 years.

Fine mineral and rock fragments are carried in suspension as a visible cloud of sediment buoyed up by the turbulence of the water. A stream's suspended load is not

Buttes, flat-topped and vertical, rise above the less-resistant material of the surrounding, eroding region.

distributed uniformly. Instead, the larger grains, such as sand, tend to concentrate closer to the bottom.

Coarse materials, including giant boulders, roll and slide along the bottom of the stream. Some particles saltate—bound or leap through the water in an arching path when a swirling eddy sweeps them from the bottom. These materials, called the bed load, are responsible for the cutting and widening of the stream's channel. Except in time of flood, the bed load does not move continuously downstream. Instead, it progresses fitfully, with many stops and starts.

The quantity of material transported by moving streams is enormous. Every year the Colorado River carries 25 million tons of debris through the Grand Canyon, and the Mississippi River dumps 730 million tons into the Gulf of Mexico.

STREAM DEPOSITION

Stream deposition occurs when there is a decrease in gradient, velocity or volume. If a stream is overloaded, if there is a change from a straight to a crooked channel, if there is an increase in channel width or an obstruction in a channel, a stream will also deposit some of its sediment. All stream deposits are known as alluvium.

Water-laid deposits are almost always stratified. If one section of the surface on which the deposits are laid is irregular, a succession of strata will lie at an angle to the general stratification. Such non-parallel stratification is called cross-bedding.

Alluvial Fans These deposits, formed by streams undergoing a sharp decrease in velocity as they emerge from highlands to more level terrain, are found around the bases of many mountains and plateaus, and in many basins— Death Valley, for instance. Alluvial fans slope downward and spread out away from the streams in fan-like fashion, varying in diameter from inches to miles, and containing material up to 17-ton boulders.

A fan that becomes steeper, thicker and coarser— developing a conical shape—is called an alluvial cone.

Sometimes adjacent alluvial fans merge to form a connected, undulating sheet of sediment along the base of a mountain range. Such a sheet is called a piedmont alluvial plain. An example is the High Plains, which extend for hundreds of miles east from the Rockies.

Deltas When a stream carrying a large load of sediment flows into a body of standing water such as a lake or ocean, its velocity declines. As a result, the stream spreads out its load in a broad, fan-shaped structure—similar to an alluvial fan—called a delta. The name delta is derived from the deposit's resemblance to the Greek letter $\triangle$.

Unlike an alluvial fan, a delta is deposited in water. Its apex points upstream. From the main stream a number of lesser streams, called distributaries, branch out into the water, each confined by low, sloping ridges called natural levees. The distributaries are separated from each other by flatlands composed of fine sediment and containing many small lakes and swamps.

Instead of displaying layers of sediment simply paralleling the lake or sea bottom, a typical delta has three sets of sediment arranged in a definite pattern. At the bottom, composed of very fine particles, are bottomset beds, which spread upon the floor in advance of the upper layers. Coarser particles, forming foreset beds, lie upon the bottomset beds at a high angle of 30° or more. Over the surface of the foreset beds are thin topset beds, which consist of clays, silts, organic material, fine sand and, sometimes, gravel.

Impressive deltas are found in the Nile, the Volga, the Tigris-Euphrates and the Danube. In China, the Hwang Ho River has built a more than 100,000-square-mile delta into the Yellow Sea. Best known in this country is the 12,000-square-mile Mississippi delta, described as a bird's-foot delta because of the striking pattern formed by its branching and rebranching distributaries and natural levees, which reach far out into the Gulf of Mexico.

Floodplains Large streams usually flow through broad, smooth lowlands which are called floodplains, because periodically the river overflows its channels and floods the valley floor. The channel is bordered with natural levees, which are built up during each flood by the river's muddy deposits. Finer silt and clay are deposited on the lower ground beyond the levees, sometimes leaving the land swampy and boggy. At the floodplain's outer limits there is frequently a border of low bluffs.

A stream may wind through a floodplain in broad, curving, S-shaped bends called meanders. Or it may subdivide around many low islands of sand and gravel deposited by the stream in its bed, rejoining and separating again and again in a braided pattern. The lower Amazon shows such an intricate pattern. So does the Arkansas where it travels between Pueblo and Dodge City. The lower part of the Arkansas River meanders, however, while still other parts run straight for short distances.

The islands around which braided streams subdivide were initially sand bars or gravel bars which trapped finer debris and reduced stream velocity, causing more deposition. Such braided channels tend to form in streams overburdened with loads too coarse to handle except during floods.

A meandering stream cuts sideways, eroding the outer (concave) bank of a bend, where it flows most rapidly, and depositing sediment on the bend's inner (convex) slope. The general tendency of meanders is to shift their positions downstream. In the course of a few hundred years, the path taken by a meandering stream may be quite different from what it is today.

Most floodplains show crescent-shaped lakes—called oxbow lakes—which are formed when a stream abandons its meander loop and takes a shortcut across the narrow neck of land at the base of the loop. (Later the oxbow lake may fill up with silt and become a bayou or swamp.) Another shortcut is the chute cut-off, formed when a flooding river rolls over its banks and flows directly across a bend.

Thick stream deposits—generally consisting of flat sheets of fine clastic sediments and occasional narrow bands of coarse sands and gravels—cover most extensive floodplains. The Lower Mississippi floodplain, for instance,

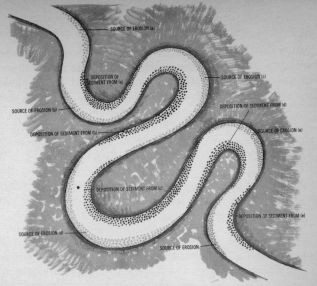

TOP: A meandering stream cuts sideways, eroding the outer (concave) bank of a bend and depositing sediment on the bend's inner (convex) slope. BOTTOM: An oxbow lake is formed when a stream abandons its meander loop and takes a shortcut. A chute cutoff is formed when a flooding river flows directly across a bend.

is built of alluvial debris from 100 feet to more than 400 feet thick.

A stream may later excavate part of its floodplain, leaving terraces standing above its new level. These remnants of the floodplain, arranged in step-like fashion in the valley, are known as stream terraces.

THE GEOMORPHIC CYCLE

Ordinarily a stream goes through successive stages in the course of its existence. Its passage from youth to maturity to old age is known as its geomorphic cycle.

Youth   A young stream is an actively eroding one, with a high gradient and many rapids and waterfalls. Running swiftly and cutting downward sharply, it carves deep V-shaped valleys into the land. There are few tributaries, no floodplains, and the elevated areas between the valleys are flat and uneroded. The turbulent Colorado River, despite its age, displays all the characteristics of youth.

Maturity   At maturity, a stream ceases its rapid downcutting. Its valley becomes more rounded in shape, and most waterfalls and rapids disappear. The stream's gradient is reduced, and as more tributaries develop, they bring in greater and greater loads of sediment. Eventually the stream is brought to grade, and all its energies are directed to carrying the load. From this point a stream's erosional activities are sideways, cutting its banks, not its bottom. At this point, too, it begins depositing surplus sediment.

Old Age   At this stage the river's gradient is very low and its load so heavy that it deposits the surplus as it meanders sluggishly across its floodplain. The surrounding land, worn low by stream erosion, has been reduced to a peneplain. Examples of old rivers are the Missouri and Mississippi.

The geomorphic cycle cannot be measured in calendar time. Some rivers stay young for a million years, while others shift rapidly from youth to maturity to old age. Many factors may speed up, slow down or even reverse the cycle. And, usually, the stream cycle moves more swiftly than the cycle of regional reduction, so that a mature stream may flow across a young landscape.

Although everyone agrees that running streams can ultimately bring down the highest mountains to almost featureless plains, the land areas of the world are clearly not in such condition. Why? Because earth's crust does not remain stationary. Instead, forces within the earth elevate portions of it, hoisting plains areas to plateaus in an unceasing duel with the reductive power of stream erosion.

Boulders take on unusual shapes when undercut by stream erosion.

Chapter 7 / Water Under the Ground

Ground water—water under the ground—is stored in the cracks and pores of rock and soil beneath the surface of the land. It fills wells with fresh water, or erupts onto the surface as geysers and springs. As it moves slowly beneath the land, ground water does a tremendous amount of geological work—cutting caverns, moving dissolved loads from place to place and depositing materials within and upon the crust of the earth.

CHARACTERISTICS OF GROUND WATER

Sources Most ground water comes from rain or snow that has soaked into the earth. This is known as meteoric water. In addition, there is a small amount of water, usually salty, that was trapped in sedimentary deposits at the time they were originally formed (connate water), and some produced by magmatic or volcanic activity (juvenile water). Although only a tiny percentage of the total precipitation becomes meteoric water, great quantities have gradually accumulated over the ages.

Distribution As water descends into the earth it passes first into a zone of aeration (or vadose zone) and then down into a zone of saturation.

In the zone of aeration the openings in rocks are filled partly with water and partly with air. The upper boundary of this zone is called the belt of soil moisture and supplies water to growing plants. Next is a region of increasing moisture content—the intermediate belt. At the lower boundary is a capillary fringe—a band of thread-like extensions of water that migrate upward from the more watery zone below.

In the zone of saturation, all holes and cracks in rocks are completely filled with water. This zone continues downward for about 5000 feet, below which the pore spaces close up and their water-holding capacity disappears.

Water Table The upper surface of the zone of saturation is called the water table. The water table is described as a subdued replica of the topography because it tends to follow the contours of the land surface, rising under hills and dipping under valleys. After a period of rain it rises nearer earth's surface; after a period of drought it subsides and flattens. In arid lands the water table may be hundreds of feet below the ground. Elsewhere it comes close to or coincides with the surface.

Movement At its greatest depths, ground water is stagnant. In regions of especially soluble rock, it may flow like a stream. But in general, ground water moves through rocks in a slow and devious fashion, following joint cracks, percolating between mineral grains and rock particles, and usually taking from 2 to 20 years to travel a mile. Important factors in the movement of ground water are a rock's porosity and its permeability.

Porosity of Rocks The total capacity of a rock to hold water is determined by its porosity. This is the ratio of a rock's solid materials to its open spaces, or voids. Porosity depends on the shape and size of a rock's grains, and on the way in which the grains are packed and cemented. (Any rock contains more water if cracked or partly dissolved.) The average amount of pore space present in sedimentary rock is 5%–10% of the rock's volume. But newly deposited muds—like those of the Mississippi Delta—may have porosities of 80%–90%. And dense, homogeneous rocks—obsidian or basalt, for instance—may have porosities as low as a few hundredths of a per cent.

Permeability of Rocks A rock's capacity to transmit ground water is its permeability. Permeability depends on the actual size—not the amount—of the openings in a rock (large ones, of course, are more permeable than small ones), and on the extent of the connections between the pore spaces. Rocks that have very small pores hold on to their water and remain impermeable, even though their porosity is high. And no matter how large the openings are, water will not flow unless they are joined together.

Clays and shales usually are classified as relatively impermeable. Sandstones, sands and gravels are considered permeable.

Perched Water   Sometimes a porous and permeable rock layer, standing above the general level of the water table, traps and holds water because it rests on an impermeable substratum that prevents the water from percolating downward. This isolated body of water, saturating the rocks within a limited area, is known as perched water. In arid regions, where permanent streams are absent, intermittent ones may flow upon perched bodies of ground water. Wells can also be dug into the rocks.

Aquifers   A body of highly porous and permeable rock or loose material through which water moves is known as an aquifer. (A rock layer too impermeable to accept water is called an aquifuge.) Most aquifers are located in the saturated zone. Usually aquifers are unconsolidated materials like sands or gravels, or beds of sandstone or limestone. But granite, if well-jointed, can supply water, and so can volcanic flows.

DISCHARGE OF GROUND WATER

Large quantities of ground water reach the surface of the earth, either artificially—through wells—or through natural discharge.

Wells are man-made holes or pits in the ground—dug or drilled to various depths—from which water can be withdrawn. The aquifer that yields water to a well may be either confined or unconfined. The two types of aquifers produce two types of wells—artesian and non-flowing.

Artesian Wells   A permeable substance—a porous, coarse-grained, loosely compacted sandstone, for instance—may be confined between layers of impermeable material, like shale. Typically the entire formation is tilted, with the permeable rock layer cropping out at the upper end in the hills or mountains. There rain water enters, then flows down through the inclined rocks at considerable pressure because of its confinement between the impermeable layers. If a hole is drilled through the shale into the sandstone, water will rise in it, forming an artesian well.

The term artesian refers to any well in which water rises above the elevation of a penetrated aquifer. Depending on topography and other circumstances, water will flow out the top of some artesian wells, while in others the water will fail to reach the surface.

The Dakota sandstone forms a confined aquifer underlying the North Central States. It reaches the surface in the Black Hills and Rocky Mountains, where rain enters and percolates down and out under the plains. Since the 1880's, when the first artesian wells were drilled into it, the Dakota sandstone has been a source of vast quantities of water. The early wells flowed freely at the surface of the ground, but now many of these wells are on the pump.

Non-flowing Wells   A water-bearing layer which is overlain by permeable material such as loam or sand is an unconfined aquifer. Water will not automatically rise in wells cut into unconfined aquifers because there is no pressure. Instead, the water always stands at water-table level and such wells must be pumped. (So must artesian wells when their flow does not reach the surface.)

The Pumping of Wells   A pumping well in an unconfined aquifer is a point of artificial discharge which disturbs the water table. If a well is heavily pumped and its water removed faster than it can be replenished, the water table is pulled down in the form of an inverted cone centered at the well. This is known as the cone of depression. The water in nearby wells will also be lowered, and some effect may be felt as far as ¼ mile away. If several wells are

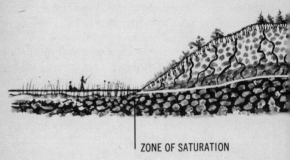

ZONE OF SATURATION

CAPILLARY FRING[E]

In the zone of aeration rock openings are filled partly
with water but in the zone of saturation water fills

pumped hard, several cones will develop and overlap, until
the water level of an entire basin is lowered. This has
happened in the southern part of the San Joaquin Valley
in California, where some 40,000 wells yield some 7 million acre feet (1 acre foot is 326,000 gallons) of ground
water per year. As a result of this excessive pumping the
water table has been lowered, in some places, as much as
250 feet since 1905.

(Note: Effects similar to the creation of a cone of
depression also occur in wells in confined aquifers.)

The natural discharge of ground water supports
permanent streams and results in the formation of springs
and geysers. Along many coast lines, fresh ground water
discharges directly onto the sea floor. Ground water may
also seep into low, spongy soil to make marshes and
swamps, which are always damp. Sometimes water fills

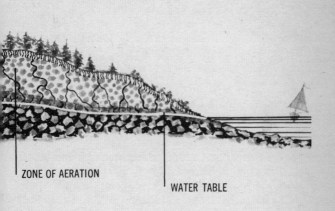

ZONE OF AERATION

WATER TABLE

all holes and cracks completely. The upper surface
of the zone of saturation is called the water table.

hollows in the land that are lower than the water table,
forming lakes or ponds.

Streams The channels of all permanent streams intersect
the dry-weather level of the water table. This is the level
beneath which the water table never sinks. If a stream
channel is too shallow to penetrate the water table, the
stream will be intermittent—running dry soon after it has
discharged its rain waters. A stream is also intermittent if
its bed lies below the upper level of the water table but
above its dry-weather level.

Sometimes the water table adds to the volume of
water in a stream. Such streams are termed effluent. Sometimes—particularly in desert or semi-arid regions—a
stream leaks water to the water table and is known as an
influent stream.

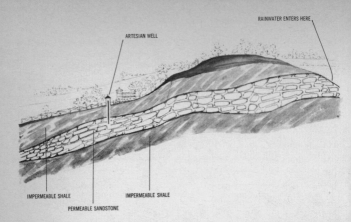

Rain water flows through the inclined rocks, confined between the impermeable layers. If a hole is drilled through the shale into the sandstone the water will rise in it, forming an artesian well.

Springs Wherever the water table intersects the ground surface, a spring is formed. When ground water is discharged in the form of springs, these springs usually appear upon hillsides or in valleys, although they can issue anywhere—even under the sea.

Like surface waters, springs range from trickles to torrents. But in general, spring water is much cleaner than natural surface waters because its slow movement through the ground filters out almost all solid impurities. It also differs from rivers and lake water in containing a larger percentage of dissolved minerals. Springs with significant quantities of such minerals are known as mineral springs.

Relative to surface waters, spring water tends to maintain a moderate and constant temperature. But sometimes springs are hot—the result of ground water coming into contact with a source of heat within the crust of the earth. Typically this source may be volcanic rocks that have not yet lost their heat. Sometimes juvenile water, freed by igneous bodies, reaches the surface as hot springs. Other hot springs are formed when rain water descends deep into the ground, and then returns quickly to the surface.

Geysers These are hot springs that erupt periodically, spouting high into the air like spectacular fountains. Practically all geyser water begins as rain which percolates below the surface, then reappears in a heated or boiling condition.

The ground water percolating downward in a geyser area travels through a complex, crooked subterranean tube that connects the land surface at one end with a source of heat at the other. This heat source may be cooling volcanic rocks, steam, or other gases given off by magma. Due to the irregularities of the tube, which interferes with the free circulation of water within it, water accumulates in the lower portion where it is heated far above the normal boiling point. This bottom water does not boil, however, because the weight of the overlying water raises the pressure and the pressure raises the boiling point.

But eventually a little of the water in the lower portion of the tube is converted into steam despite the high pressure. When the water becomes steam it expands, forcing the water in the tube upward and over the rim. This spill-over reduces the pressure throughout the column, with the result that the superheated water flashes into steam and hurls skyward a mixture of steam and hot water. Eruption continues until the superheated steam has escaped and the passageways are filled with cool air. Then the cycle of heating and eruption begins again.

The three great geyser regions of the world are Yellowstone National Park in Wyoming, New Zealand and Iceland. Geysers also occur in Mexico, the Azores, South America, Japan and a few other places. In Yellowstone there are about 200 geysers—some extremely unpredictable, others erupting on regular schedule. Most famous of these is Old Faithful, which shoots out a column of scalding water nearly 150 feet into the air about every 65 seconds.

GROUND-WATER EROSION

Ground water charged with the carbonic acid contained in rain readily dissolves such rocks as limestone, dolomite, marble, gypsum and salt. In removing these materials, ground water acts as an agent of erosion.

Caves All the large caves in the world have been created by the dissolving action of ground water. Caves are big subterranean openings in soluble rock layers—primarily limestone—which generally form a network of "rooms" and passageways, sometimes at several different levels.

How, precisely, caves develop has not yet been settled, although many geologists subscribe to the "two-cycle" theory of cave origin. The theory posits, first, a cycle during which rocks are dissolved by circulating ground water below the water table. This is followed by a second cycle, which begins when the cavern emerges above the water table, either because the water table is lowered or the land is uplifted. At this stage, enlargement of the cave may continue through the erosional activity of underground streams. At the same time, calcium carbonate or other soluble compounds accumulate on the cavern's walls, ceiling and floor.

Caves can be found in many parts of the world, with some notable examples in this country. A cave region of about 8000 square miles exists in Kentucky, southern Indiana and northern Tennessee, where out of a thick, nearly horizontal limestone bed, thousands of caves have been dissolved. Most famous of these is Mammoth Cave, near Bowling Green, Kentucky, which features streams, lakes and waterfalls, and more than 150 miles of tunnels.

In New Mexico, Carlsbad Cavern is noted for its beautifully decorated interior and its great size. More than 1300 feet deep in places, it contains a single room 350 feet high, 625 feet wide and 4000 feet long.

Sink Holes Regions underlain by thick limestone beds often display funnel-shaped or irregular depressions known as sinks or sink holes. These depressions occur when percolating ground water seeping downward along joints dissolves and carries away rock. (Sink holes are also formed when the rock roof of a cavern suddenly collapses.)

In New Mexico, the Carlsbad Caverns are noted for their beautifully decorated interior and their great size.

Sometimes sink holes are floored with clay and can hold small lakes. Sometimes they intercept the water table at depths of perhaps hundreds of feet and serve as natural wells.

Natural Bridges   The solvent action of ground water is responsible, at times, for the formation of natural bridges. Adjacent sink holes draining into subterranean cavities may enlarge and merge, and the surface rock separating the depressions may thus become a bridge. On rare occasions the collapse of a cavern's roof results in a natural bridge formed by the surviving portion.

Karst Topography   Regions underlain by limestone may develop a number of features not found in regions of less soluble rock. The resulting formations are known as karst topography, named for the Karst region of Yugoslavia along the Adriatic Coast. Karst regions are pockmarked with sink holes and honeycombed with underground caverns. Surface streams vanish below, sometimes reappearing as giant springs. Other karst features are tunnels, grottoes, natural bridges and underground pools and falls. The Causses Plateau of southern France west of the Rhone River is a well-known karst region. In this country karst topography is represented in Florida, Kentucky and southern Indiana, where in some places more than a thousand sink holes per square mile can be found.

GROUND-WATER TRANSPORTATION

By moving dissolved minerals in solution from place to place, ground water acts as an agent of transportation. Dissolved limestone is carried by ground water in the form of calcium bicarbonate. But highly soluble rocks are not the only ones that are dissolved and transported by ground water. Given enough time, even highly insoluble minerals will go into solution.

GROUND-WATER DEPOSITION

At any point along its route, ground water may deposit the mineral matter it carries in solution. Deposition occurs when ground water evaporates or is saturated.

Cementation   Ground water plays an important role in the consolidation of sedimentary rock. When calcite, silica or iron oxide are deposited in the pore spaces of unconsolidated sediments, they serve as natural cements, transforming loose materials into solid rock.

Stalactites, Stalagmites and Pillars   These strikingly beautiful formations are the most outstanding of ground-water deposits. Stalactites, which hang from cave ceilings like giant icicles, usually form when dripping water seeps from the rocks above the cave and either evaporates or loses its carbon dioxide to the air. In either case a tiny ring of calcium carbonate is deposited, followed by another and another, until a pendant-shaped stalactite is produced.

Stalagmites are deposits of calcium carbonate that grow upward as drops of water spatter to the floor of the cave. The forms of stalagmites are usually stumpier and more varied than those of stalactites.

Sometimes a downward-growing stalactite and an upward-growing stalagmite meet in the middle and fuse. The floor to ceiling formation that results is called a pillar or column. Sheets and ribbons and draperies and other interesting shapes may also be formed in caverns by ground-water deposits.

Concretions   Concretions are nodular masses in sedimentary rocks which develop when ground-water deposits occur around a grain of sand, or a fossil, or some other nucleus. Concretions range in size from microscopic to several feet. They may be disc-shaped, spherical, cylindrical or irregular, sometimes resembling an animal or vegetable. As concretions grow, they may slowly replace the host rock.

Geodes   These are cavities in rocks which are lined with inward-pointing crystals, most commonly of quartz or calcite. Geodes are, in effect, miniature caves.

Petrifaction   Mineral matter such as silica, deposited by ground water, may replace the cells in wood, bones, shells or leaves particle by particle, forming a precise mineral copy of the original. Replacement of once deeply buried logs by deposited mineral matter is responsible for the Petrified Forest National Monument of Arizona.

Hot Water Deposits   The orifices of geysers and hot springs are frequently surrounded by ground-water deposits. If the deposits come directly from the mineral-rich geyser water, they are usually composed of grayish-colored silica and are called siliceous sinter. Travertine deposits, frequently colored red, brown, yellow or black due to impurities, are made by calcareous (limy) algae able to survive the high temperatures of the hot springs.

WATER WITCHING

Many geologists writing about ground water feel it necessary to take the trouble to debunk the claims of "dowsers," "water witches" and "diviners." These are individuals who maintain they can locate veins of water below the surface of the earth by using a forked twig which will dip violently when the channel of an underground stream is crossed. They further maintain that they can estimate the depth of the water by the number of times the divining rod dips.

Dowsing is at least as old as the fifteenth century and was probably practiced far earlier in man's history. For centuries farmers consulted with dowsers before digging a well. Even today, a belief in water witching persists, and is affirmed annually at the convention of the American Society of Dowsers.

Since ground water is, in effect, all over the place, dowsers have met with considerable success over the years. But there is no scientific basis for what dowsers do, nor do most of them seem to understand anything about the true nature and occurrence of ground water. Like wishing wells, water witching is an attractive notion but, say the geologists very firmly, it has nothing to do with geology.

Chapter 8 / Glaciers Shape the Land

Within the past million years—geologists think this figure may now be two or more million—great masses of ice flowed across northern Europe and northern North America, burying tall mountains, leveling entire forests, forcing men and beasts to flee before them. The ice retreated, then returned—again, and again, and again—to lap up the helpless land with its frigid tongue.

During this geological age, known as the Pleistocene, ice blanketed one-third of earth's land surface—some 18–20 million square miles. Today only one-tenth of the earth is glaciated, and the giant continental ice sheets have backed up to Greenland and Antarctica.

The vanished ice sheets have left behind filed valleys, jagged peaks, gouged lake basins, displaced boulders and a wide and vivid assortment of glacial deposits. They have carried off vast amounts of soil, leaving one region stripped and barren, another enriched. In today's more modest glaciers, the diligent geological work of the Ice Age continues.

FORMATION OF GLACIERS

There are glaciers in the equatorial mountains of Kilimanjaro in Africa, the Andes in South America and the Carstenz Toppenz Range in New Guinea at heights of 16,000–18,000 feet. Glaciers are also found in the middle latitudes—the Sierras and the Swiss Alps—at 9000 feet. In the borderlands of the Arctic Ocean glaciers stand at about 1500 feet, and in Antarctica they reach sea level.

In all these regions, the temperature remains below freezing for much of the year, and snowfall is heavy. The climate permits the accumulation of extensive, almost motionless bodies of snow—called snowfields—which are eventually transformed into glacial ice. There are no permanent snowfields and glaciers in North Greenland (although almost all the rest of the country is glaciated) because, despite the low mean annual temperatures, snowfall is too scanty.

Glacial ice develops not from water but from snow. First, the light powdery snowflakes melt and refreeze, forming gritty, bird-shot-size pellets of ice called firn or neve. Then new snow falls, increasing the pressure upon the firn. Deep in the snowfield, the individual ice grains come into closer contact with each other as the pore space between them is reduced. At the same time, the grains recrystallize. Finally, the granules of white or grayish-white firn are welded together into solid, bluish glacial ice.

TYPES OF GLACIERS

Glaciers are thick, slow-moving masses of ice. They may be alpine glaciers (either valley or piedmont), confined to valleys in mountainous regions and moving downslope under the promptings of gravity. Or they may be ice caps and continental glaciers, which cover broad areas and spread outward in all directions from a center of accumulation.

Valley Glaciers   These are long, narrow ice streams, held between the steep walls of a mountain valley and fed from above by large snowfields. They are found in every continent but Australia, moving downward through a trough previously formed by a stream. Valley glaciers perched on the edge of cliffs are called cliff or hanging glaciers. Those that end in the ocean, where they serve as a source of icebergs, are called tidal or tidewater glaciers.

The best-known valley glaciers are found in the Alps. The Himalayas and Alaska boast some that are 30–70 miles long and over 3000 feet thick. In the United States, long ice streams surround the summit of Washington's Mount Rainier, but in general our valley glaciers are relatively short and narrow.

Piedmont Glaciers   These rather rare glaciers form when the snout of a valley glacier spreads out in a bulbous form,

Long ice streams surround the summit of Washington's Mount Rainier. Note the medial moraine on the lower right hand side.

or when several valley glaciers coalesce at the foot of a mountain and sprawl onto the adjacent lowlands in a broad apron of ice. Largest of the piedmont glaciers is Alaska's nearly stagnant Malaspina—a lobate ice mass covering about 1400 square miles.

Ice Caps   These small masses of radially spreading ice are found in Iceland, Spitsbergen, parts of Scandinavia and on the islands north of Canada.

Continental Glaciers   Today's continental ice sheets—the most extensive of all glaciers—are confined to Greenland (except for its northern tip) and Antarctica.

Greenland's ice sheet, about 700,000 square miles, occupies approximately 83% of Greenland. It flows from two dome-shaped high points, in places spilling into the sea and becoming icebergs. One such berg took 1489 lives when it sank the unsinkable *Titanic* in 1912. If all of Greenland's glacial ice were melted, the sea level throughout the world would rise by 21 feet. Measurements indicate, however, that the Greenland ice sheet is expanding.

Antarctica's continental glacier, about 5,000,000 square miles, covers almost all its surface area and displays, at one point, the greatest ice thickness found on earth—14,000 feet. There is enough water locked up in Antarctica's glacial ice to raise the level of the oceans about 195 feet. But measurements seem to indicate that this continental glacier, too, is growing.

Antarctica is fringed with floating masses of glacier ice, called ice shelves, which are attached to the main ice sheet. These include the two largest ice shelves in the world—Ross Ice Shelf (200,000 square miles, about the size of Spain) and Filchner Ice Shelf (160,000 square miles).

GLACIER EROSION

Methods of Erosion   Glaciers erode by quarrying (also called plucking) and by abrasion. In quarrying, blocks of bedrock are dislodged. In abrasion, bedrock is scratched and ground by rock fragments imbedded in the glacier. Generally speaking, quarrying seems more effective at a

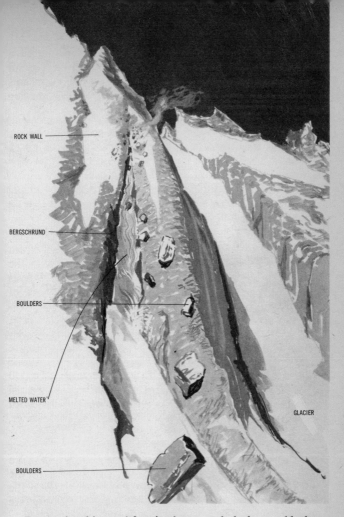

ROCK WALL

BERGSCHRUND

BOULDERS

MELTED WATER

GLACIER

BOULDERS

Repeated melting and freezing loosen and pluck away blocks of rock from the bergschrund's upstream wall; these free rocks are then incorporated into the glacier and carried off.

glacier's upper end, while abrasion seems more effective downstream.

Rocks are quarried through the process known as frost-wedging, which occurs within the crevasses and bergschrunds of glaciers. Crevasses are cracks which start at a glacier's brittle surface and extend downward as much as 150 feet. At the head of most valley glaciers, a deep crescent-shaped crevasse, called a bergschrund, is commonly found.

Bergschrunds have a rocky wall on the upstream side and an ice wall on the other. The rock wall is shattered and riven with joints, into which melting snow pours during the day, then freezes when temperatures drop at night. Repeated melting and freezing eventually loosens blocks of rock from the rocky headwall or glacier floor and plucks them away. These free rocks are then incorporated into the glacier and carried off when it moves downslope.

As a glacier flows along, it carries abrasive rock debris of every size. The large chunks gouge and scratch, marking the land with grooves or scratches called striations. These are clearly exhibited on Mount Kearsarge in New Hampshire, where ice once rode over the top of this 2937-foot peak. The fine-grained bits of debris abrade the land by polishing surfaces smooth and shiny. Glaciers have given the higher parts of Yosemite National Park a bright, polished sheen.

Erosional Landforms Quarrying steepens slopes and sharpens peaks and ridges. Abrasion smooths irregularities in the land and deepens valleys into U-shaped troughs.

When a valley glacier melts, exposing its headwall (the steep wall where the glacier begins), it displays a distinctive feature of glacial erosion—the cirque. This is a steep-walled, horseshoe-shaped hollow cut in the side of a mountain, bordered by high, curving, jagged and shattered cliffs. Cirques result from active plucking in the bergschrund zone. They are found in every glaciated mountain area.

Sometimes cirques cut headward from opposite sides of a mountain, drawing closer until they almost meet back to back. Eventually all that stands between them is a narrow, knife-edged ridge called an arête, frequently topped with small pinnacles nicknamed *gendarmes* by French-speaking alpinists. The Continental Divide follows an arête known as the Garden Wall in Montana's Glacier National Park.

If an arête is eroded, the cirques will meet and intersect, forming a mountain pass known as a col (neck). St. Bernard, St. Gothard and Simplon are glacially created passes found in the Alps.

When glaciers erode unevenly, they may cut out basins which subsequently fill with water. These rock-basin lakes, known as tarns, are common on cirque floors or along the bottoms of smaller glacial troughs. An example is Iceberg Lake in Glacier National Park.

A horn is a jagged pinnacle, the eroded remains of a tall mountain peak whittled away by a number of glaciers radiating outward from its summit. No representative of horns surpasses the one that named them all—Switzerland's world-famous Matterhorn.

A typical sign of a stream valley's erosion by glacier is the alteration of its profile from V-shaped to U-shaped, with smoothed and steepened sides. A good example is the valley below Garmisch in the Bavarian Alps. In the United States, the dramatic U-shaped incision of Yosemite Valley testifies to the power of Ice Age glaciers.

Tributary valleys, occupied by smaller glaciers or none at all, do not deepen as rapidly as the main valley and so may become suspended over it. These erosional forms are called hanging valleys, and often serve as the later sites of waterfalls. In Norway many beautiful falls—like the Seven Sisters Falls in Geirangerfjord—plunge from hanging valleys into fjords.

A fjord is formed when a glacier erodes its valley floor below sea level, then melts, permitting the mouth of the valley to be occupied by the sea. Fjords, then, are simply drowned, glacially produced, U-shaped valleys, sometimes thousands of feet deep. The fjords of Norway are particularly famous, but fjords are found, too, in Alaska, British Columbia, Scotland, Greenland, and along the western coast of South America.

Still other, very common forms produced by glaciers are the giant (cyclopean) steps. They are formed along the length of a valley floor as the result of differential erosion. There are also the *roches moutonnées* (or sheep rocks), such as those displayed in granite at Lake Shore, Ontario. These are rounded humps of rocks named for their resemblance to a flock of grazing sheep.

Roches moutonnées show clearly that glaciers once passed their way. On the side from which the glacier approached, the rock is smooth and polished and gently sloping. The other side, protected from the glacial rasp, is steeper and far more irregular.

GLACIER TRANSPORTATION

Nature of Flow   At and near a glacier's surface—in the zone of fracture—glacial ice is rigid because temperatures are low and pressure is slight. Within the glacier, however, in the zone of flow—pressure makes the ice plastic. As a result a glacier is capable of flowing (as a solid flows) under its own weight, rafting along the brittle crevassed ice on top. While the mechanism of glacial flow is unclear, it seems to involve the freezing, unfreezing and refreezing of ice crystals, the downslope slippage of individual crystals and the mechanical sliding of the ice mass along its bed.

Glacial ice begins to flow downhill and spread out under its own weight when only a few dozen feet of solid ice have built up beneath a cover of firn and snow. Glacier motion is imperceptible, with extremes ranging from near stagnant to speeds of more than 150 feet a day. Glaciers travel faster in summer and during the daytime, when the temperatures are higher.

Scientists have proven that glaciers do indeed move, by driving a straight row of stakes across them. In time the line of stakes becomes crooked, bent in the direction of the glacier's flow, with the greatest displacement occurring in the center, where speed is highest. Switzerland's largest glacier, the Great Aletsch, advances about 20 inches a day. The Rhone glacier moves about 300 feet a year. In parts of Greenland the ice travels 5 miles per year—a rate of 80 feet each day.

The headward portion of a glacier is its zone of accumulation. At its foot—the zone of wastage—melting and evaporation (together called ablation) occur, and so does the calving of icebergs, which float off to sea.

A glacier is said to advance when it moves forward more rapidly than its foot (its front section) melts. A glacier recedes when its foot melts faster than the ice moves forward. A glacier achieves a state of dynamic equilibrium when the forward motion is equaled by the melting back.

Glacier Load As the glacial ice moves along, it serves as an agent of transportation. A glacier usually transports a far smaller quantity of foreign material than does a river of similar size. But its ability to move large rocks is far greater. Carrying power and velocity, related in rivers, are unrelated in glaciers, and so boulders are transported as readily as tiny rock flour.

A glacier carries material on its surface, at its base and in between. Rocks frozen within the body of a glacier are known as the englacial load.

The glacier surface usually contains rock debris worn from the valley walls. This debris forms distinctive dark bands, called moraines, parallel to the direction of glacier flow. If the bands appear along the sides of glaciers they are known as lateral moraines. If two valley glaciers converge, the inner lateral moraines will unite to form a medial moraine at or near the glacier's center. Sometimes several tributary glaciers merge, creating several medial moraines. There are many outstanding medial moraines on Barnard Glacier in Alaska's St. Elias Mountains.

In alpine glaciers, most of the transported debris is concentrated in the medial and lateral moraines. But glaciers also carry a lot of rock debris scattered throughout the ice, particularly near their floors. Much of this is loose rock and soil plucked and rasped by the glacier as it erodes its way downslope.

A glacier's load may produce interesting surface features on the ice. Small dust piles and rock particles, warmed by the sun, often sink into the surface, forming depressions called dust wells. On the other hand, rocks too large to conduct heat may shade the ice on which they rest and create rock-topped ice pedestals called glacier tables, which stand up long after the surrounding ice has melted away.

GLACIER DEPOSITS

A melting glacier leaves behind various deposits formed below the ice and at its front. All glacial deposits are grouped under the term drift, a name that was selected back in the days when the work of glaciers was erroneously attributed to the biblical Flood. Floating icebergs, so the story went, "drifted" through the ancient waters, dropping their load of debris when they melted.

Glacial drift is classified as non-stratified and stratified.

Non-stratified Drift   The glacial debris that composes non-stratified drift is called till, unsorted and unlayered material that is deposited directly by ice without the aid of water. Till consists of everything from boulders to fine material.

Till usually occurs in a regular, generally linear land form called a moraine. (The word moraine was also used earlier to describe the loads carried by glaciers.) Moraines are formed by both valley and continental glaciers.

Terminal or end moraines are curving, elongated, usually discontinuous ridges marking the foremost position of the ice. Examples are found in the Great Lakes regions, which are festooned for many miles with terminal moraines deposited by continental glaciers during the Pleistocene. In Britain the largest end moraine is Cromer Ridge, northeast of London. It is 15 miles long and stands 300 feet tall.

Sometimes hollows pit the surface of end moraines or appear in the land around them. These depressions, called kettles, are produced when buried, isolated blocks of ice melt, causing the layer of glacial debris atop them to collapse into the hollows created. Kettles range from a few feet to several hundred feet across, sometimes filling with water to form small lakes or ponds. Kettles and other irregularities in the glacially produced ground of an end moraine create a bumpy-looking landscape described as knob-and-basin topography.

As the ice retreats, it leaves a series of ridges, known as recessional moraines, behind the terminal moraines. Each recessional moraine indicates a temporary halt in the backward march of the glacier. On Long Island, New York, the Ronkonkoma and Harbor Hill ridges are recessional moraines.

Both terminal and recessional moraines may curve around the snout of a valley glacier and up its sides, forming lateral moraines.

End moraines and lateral moraines often serve as effective dams long after the ice has disappeared. Moraine-blocked waters include such scenic alpine lakes as Como, Maggiore, Garda, Geneva and Luzerne. In the United States Lake Mary and Lake MacDonald, both in Glacier National Park, are outstanding examples of moraine damming. The Great Lakes were formed, in part, in this way.

Sometimes till is irregularly scattered in a broad sheet across the former path of a glacier instead of being aligned in neat ridges. Part of this debris was dropped from the bottom of an active glacier as it moved forward; part was left when stagnant ice melted downward from its surface. The total material constitutes a ground moraine, the most widespread deposit of a continental ice sheet.

A ground moraine may display broad expanses of barren rock, with gouged-out basins holding lakes. Sometimes the topography is pocked with kettle holes; sometimes the surface is quite level.

A distinctive geometrical feature of ground moraines is the drumlin, a mass of subglacial debris (all till or till with a core of bedrock) molded beneath the ice. Drumlins are streamlined, with half-an-egg-shaped ridges, rarely more than ½ mile long and 100 feet high. They commonly occur in groups, their long axes parallel to the flow of the ice. Large groups are found in New York, Massachusetts, Wisconsin, Michigan and the British Isles. Bunker Hill is a renowned drumlin.

The rock fragments in till are not rounded like the pebbles carried by streams and ocean water. Instead, they are sharply angular. Those dragged along the bedrock floor are striated and show one or more flat, grooved and polished surfaces, called facets.

Among the boulders composing till may be some that are entirely foreign to the bedrock on which they stand. These displaced rocks, which have sometimes traveled long distances, are called erratics. In Nottingham, New Hampshire, an erratic measures 60 feet long and 40 feet wide and high, with an estimated weight of 6000 tons. Another, in Madison, New Hampshire, is 30 feet by 40 by 90. Basalt boulders, standing upon the mica schist bedrock of New York City's Central Park, are erratics glacier-borne across the Hudson River from the Palisades.

Stratified Drift This is glacial debris deposited by melt-water from the glacier and accumulated in streams issuing from the ice (glaciofluvial deposits), in temporary lakes along the ice border (glaciolacustrine deposits) and in the sea at the margins of the glaciated region (glaciomarine deposits). Unlike till, these deposits are sorted and layered. An important ingredient of stratified drift is rock flour—finely ground material pulverized by glacial abrasion.

At the outer margin of many terminal moraines are outwash plains, built by debris-laden meltwater streaming away from the glacier's ice front. Gravel and sand are spread out in a series of alluvial fans, which merge to form a broad, apron-shaped plain displaying a network of braided channels. These plains of glacially derived, water-laid sediment may be pitted by kettle holes, but often they are level and featureless, with fine-grained, uniformly textured, very fertile soil. Most of the good farmland in the Midwest is derived from outwash plains.

A valley train, which may extend far beyond the end of a particular valley, is a smaller version of an out-wash plain.

Kames are irregular hills associated with end moraines. They were formed when meltwater piled up cones and alluvial fans of glacial debris at the edges of great slabs and blocks of stagnant or "dead" ice—the unmoving remains of waning glaciers melting downward from the surface. When the ice finally melted away, the unsupported sand and gravel slumped, forming irregularly stratified hillocks.

Kame terraces form between the dead ice at the sides of a glacier and the adjoining valley walls. After the ice vanishes, they stand above the valley.

Meltwaters also flow in tunnels within or beneath the dead ice. They deposit part of their load along the channels, piling it between the supporting ice walls. When the ice melts, the deposits stand as long, narrow, steep-sided, round-topped ridges of poorly sorted and layered sand and gravel called eskers. These may be a few feet high and a few hundred yards long, or 100–200 feet high and dozens of miles long. Winding eskers, looking like old railroad embankments, traverse the land in Scandinavia, Finland, Maine, Wisconsin and elsewhere. Both kames and eskers are excellent sources of sand and gravel for construction work.

Crevasse fillings are like eskers, but form in ice valleys instead of ice tunnels. They are rarely more than a mile long.

Proglacial lakes may fringe the border of a retreating glacier in hollows in its outwash plain, between the end of the ice and the terminal moraines and in valleys damned by moraines. These lakes collect sediments laid down by meltwater streams in cycles—a relatively coarse layer (deposited during spring and summer) covered with a thinner, finer layer (deposited in winter and fall). A pair of such bands—together called a varve—represents the sediment of one year. Varves, like tree rings, help to establish a chronology.

THE GREAT ICE AGE

The scoured and striated bedrock, the cirques and the moraines, the kames and the eskers, the innumerable lakes and marshes, the startling erratics—all testify to the presence of past ice. But it was only little more than a century ago, thanks to the work of European geologists Ignaz Venetz and Jean de Chapentier and Swiss naturalist Louis Agassiz, that the existence of a Great Ice Age was recognized.

It is known today that the Pleistocene was not one massive assault of ice, but at least four major advances. It is believed that continental ice last withdrew from the Great Lakes region about 11,000 years ago. (Evidence also indicates two previous periods of widespread glaciation in earth's history—during the late Paleozoic and the late Precambrian.)

At least 50 hypotheses—both geological and astronomical—have attempted to explain the causes of Pleistocene glaciation. None are universally accepted. Nor do we even know where we currently stand in relation to the glacial cycle. Are we living in another interglacial epoch, to be followed by still another invasion of the ice? Or will the remaining glaciers on our planet melt, unleashing vast quantities of water to drown coastal cities and plains in a shallow sea?

Chapter 9 / Wind and the Deserts

Wind is the atmosphere in motion, free to wander un-confined all over the planet. As it moves it picks up, carries off and deposits, doing its most conspicuous work in arid lands. Geologists like to say, though they won't try to prove it, that every square mile of land on earth is covered with at least one speck of dust from every other square mile, carried there by the action of blowing winds.

WIND EROSION

Wind erodes through deflation and abrasion.

Deflation This process simply involves the lifting away of loose, light particles of rock and soil. As the finer par-ticles are carried off, the denuded regions display a cover-ing of coarse gravel and stones—materials too large for wind transport. Such a surface is called a lag gravel or desert pavement, and may occupy anywhere from a small area to several hundred square miles.

Sometimes the wind's lifting and removing action will excavate basins—known as blowouts—in soft, unconsoli-dated or poorly cemented materials, particularly when unimpeded by vegetation or lag gravel. Rain may fill up blowouts with water, forming lakes or ponds.

Ordinarily, wind-carved depressions are only a few feet deep. But there are some striking examples of enor-mous basins cut by the wind in arid lands. An impressive deflated basin is the great oasis of Kharga in the Sahara, west of the Nile. Although wind erosion was probably not responsible for hollowing out the entire thing, it played a prominent role in enlarging it to its present proportions —120 miles long, 12–50 miles wide and 600–1000 feet deep. Another remarkable basin excavated by the wind is the imposing Qattara Depression, a saline trough covering 7500 square miles.

Deflation continues until the water table is reached. Once the ground becomes damp, the wind cannot readily pick up loose material.

The effects of deflation were spectacularly evident in the great dust storms of the 1930's, which blew out the notorious Dust Bowl of Kansas, Oklahoma, Nebraska and other Plains States. A succession of dry seasons, combined with faulty farming practices, left extensive areas parched, bare of crops and uncohesive. Across this utterly vulnerable land swept the wind, plucking away great clouds of dust and driving them toward the Atlantic. In one dust storm alone, more than 300 million tons of soil were removed and scattered over the land and sea to the East.

Abrasion   Although the chief role of wind erosion is the removal of unconsolidated materials, wind also has the capacity to abrade. This is the smoothing, polishing, pitting or etching of exposed rock faces standing in the path of sand- and silt-laden wind. Wind abrasion is most effective within a few feet of the ground, where the heavier part of the load is carried. Stones and boulders subjected to wind abrasion are known as ventifacts.

Wind abrasion frequently works with weathering and rainwash to sculpt fantastic forms in arid lands. Rocks of varied composition and texture may be shaped into knobs, "statues" and pillars—known in some places as hoodoos —by the abrasive action of the wind.

WIND TRANSPORTATION

Wind velocities range from zero to more than 100 miles an hour, from the dead calm that immobilizes sailboats to raging hurricanes that tear up the coast. Experiments indicate that it requires a wind velocity of 11 miles an hour to move a fine particle of sand 0.25 millimeter in diameter. At velocities of 20–30 miles an hour, winds accomplish important geologic work.

Unlike streams and glaciers, winds are incapable of carrying boulders, gravel, or even—except under special

The loess deposits of the Vicksburg quadrangle in the Mississippi Valley come from the once-glaciated northern states.

conditions—pebbles. Nevertheless they can carry finer materials—sand, silt and dust. Materials are transported by the wind as either bed load or suspended load.

Bed Load Most of this load is not dust but grains of silt and sand—material too large or too heavy to be lifted any significant distance off the ground. These particles roll or slide along the surface or move by a process called saltation, a series of successive leaps. As one particle falls to the ground, it dislodges another, continuing the forward motion of the load until wind velocity drops. Even in a severe storm, wind-blown sand particles rarely rise more than 6 feet.

Suspended Load Lighter, smaller particles, principally dust, are carried in suspension. These particles travel higher and farther and longer than the bed load. Dust from volcanic eruptions· may ride the wind for years, thousands of feet from the ground, sometimes giving a deep red color to the sunset. Topsoil may be held in suspension for

weeks. Winds have occasionally whirled dust all the way from the Sahara to England—a distance of 2000 miles.

WIND DEPOSITION

As wind loses velocity, or is washed with rain, it deposits its load of sand and silt and dust. Apart from an occasional deposit of volcanic dust, the most significant wind-blown (aeolian) deposits are loess and sand dunes.

Loess These deposits are composed chiefly of silt-sized particles of angular minerals and rock fragments. They are loam-like, basically unconsolidated and unstratified, and yellowish-buff in color. Loess deposits may blanket hundreds of thousands of square miles, in some places measuring many hundreds of feet thick. Despite its lack of coherence, loess can stand in nearly vertical walls and cliffs.

Loess deposits are made up of materials transported

from deserts or from regions of glacial outwash, where glacial debris was pulverized but not chemically altered. The most famous loess deposits are found in North China, windborne from the Gobi Desert. The loess deposits of the Mississippi Valley come from the once-glaciated northern states.

Other areas of widespread loess deposits occur in Germany, Russia and Turkestan. Loessial soils make fertile farming land—the soils of Iowa, Illinois and Indiana, for instance. Loess is responsible for the coloration that has named the Yellow River and Yellow Sea.

Sand Dunes Due to the subtle sorting power of the wind, sand dunes are built predominantly of sand-sized grains. Lighter materials are blown farther away, while coarser rock fragments lag behind as lag gravel.

Most dunes contain a large proportion of quartz grains. Interesting exceptions are Bermuda's calcite dunes, and the gypsum "white sands" of southern New Mexico. Sand dunes tend to be light in color—white, yellow, gray, occasionally red—and contain few or no fossils. Distinctive ripples frequently mark their surface, and individual grains have a frosted appearance. Most dunes are steep on the lee (downwind) side and gentle on the windward (upwind) side. They may be only a few feet tall, or rise several hundred feet into the sky.

Some sand deposits are climbing dunes, formed where the wind must rise over a sharp topographic break. Other sand deposits are falling dunes, formed where sand sweeps over a cliff into a wind-protected hollow. Sand dunes also build up in wide, flat plains.

Dunes achieve their best development in desert regions, with dunes of great size abounding in the Arabian and Sahara deserts. But they also exist at the seashore (along much of the Atlantic Coast), beside lakes (the eastern shore of Lake Michigan, for instance) and bordering the sandy plains of some large rivers like the Volga.

There are active dunes, still in the process of formation, and inactive or stabilized dunes.

Sand dunes of pure gypsum, "white sands," are found in southern New Mexico.

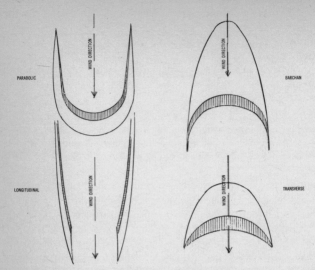

The most common stabilized dune is the parabolic dune, while active dunes include barchans, transverse dunes, and longitudinal dunes.

Active dunes change their shapes and positions on the ground. As new material is added to the windward side and rolls over the crest and down its lee slope, these dunes migrate in the direction of the wind, at speeds ranging from a few feet to more than 100 feet per year. Creeping dunes have buried farmlands, railroads and even villages in the United States, France and elsewhere, and have smothered ancient cities in central Asia and Africa.

Inactive dunes have a vegetational cover which helps to fix their position and their shape. These dunes may indicate an alteration in climate from arid to more humid.

Active dunes include barchans, transverse dunes and longitudinal dunes, as well as complex dunes of irregular shape. Irregular-shaped dunes occur in areas of frequently changing winds. When the winds blow steadily from one direction, dunes take on more enduring forms.

Barchans are crescent-shaped dunes—the horns pointing downwind—characteristic of desert regions with small supplies of sand and moderate winds. Uniform, perfectly shaped barchans can be seen in Peru's La Joya Desert.

Transverse dunes are aligned at right angles to the wind direction. These short dunes develop where strong winds blow and the sand supply is abundant. Many coastal dunes are transverse.

Longitudinal dunes, long ridges parallel to the wind direction, are formed where strong winds blow and sand and vegetation are sparse. They appear in the Great Sandy Desert of Australia.

The most common stabilized dune is the parabolic or U-shaped dune, whose points, unlike those of the barchan, point upwind. While erosion continues in its central blowout zone, vegetation develops over its outer slopes, ultimately anchoring the dune in place. Stabilized or partly stabilized dunes greatly exceed the number of active dunes in the United States. The largest extent of stabilized dunes in this country is found in Nebraska, in an area called Sand Hills. Another impressive tract appears along the eastern coast of Lake Michigan, where some of the dunes rise more than 150 feet.

THE DESERTS

Not surprisingly, wind is most effective in the arid regions of the world, where the ground surface is relatively unprotected by vegetation or a sturdy blanket of weathered soil. But contrary to popular belief, most deserts are not sandy but rocky. And despite desert drought, the most important geological work in arid lands is achieved not by wind but by streams.

Deserts occupy about one-sixth of the earth's land surface. Most of them are found in the subtropical belts of high atmospheric pressure—cloudless zones of high evaporation, low precipitation and drying winds. Some deserts, like those in parts of our West, stand in the "rain shadow" of tall mountains, where moisture-laden clouds climbing the peaks are wrung dry before they ever reach the other side. Deserts are also formed because of cold coastal currents, such as the Humboldt Current off the Atacama Desert of Chile and Peru, or the Benguela Current of Africa's Kalahari.

Only the biggest of rivers—like the Nile, the Indus,

the Colorado, the Niger—can survive the journey through the desert to the sea. For the most part, deserts are characterized by interior drainage—small stream systems which never travel beyond the desert's boundaries. Instead, the water evaporates, sinks into the sand or forms stagnant pools, salt lakes or alkali mud flats.

Desert lakes tend to be brackish or saline. They range in size from tiny ponds to the Great Salt Lake with its 2000-square-mile surface area. In exceptionally dry periods, the lake level drops, leaving a border of salt, like the Bonneville Salt Flat adjacent to the Great Salt Lake.

It is true that much of the desert scenery we see today was created in the past at a time when considerably more water washed the land. But even the limited rain that currently falls does important geological work.

Erosion   A moderate rain in the desert may behave like a cloudburst, swiftly cutting ravines, arroyos and gullies. An erosional form characteristic of our deserts is the pediment, a broad, gently sloping surface carved in the bedrock at the foot of a relatively steep mountain slope. The pediment is produced by years upon years of degradation and rock removal.

Another erosional landform is the inselberg, a small and isolated hill. This shrunken remnant of a former mountain rises above the desert's planed-off rock surface.

Theoretically, if no climatic or structural changes occurred, a desert could eventually be reduced to a wide rock plain. But so far no large desert area on earth has achieved this final erosional stage.

Transportation   Desert cloudbursts fill up arroyos with violently swirling streams capable of sweeping along great masses of debris. Sometimes the banks of channels are overtopped and a sheet of muddy, turbulent water spills onto the desert floor. But even a dozen feet of water in an arroyo will sink into the soil or be dried by the desert sun within only a few hours of the storm's beginning.

Deposition   Because of the system of interior drainage, running water does not move debris out of the desert and into the sea. Instead, materials are carried for only short distances and are then deposited within the desert's confines.

Boulders, gravel and sand form alluvial fans, a characteristic stream deposit in deserts. The water may percolate through the pore spaces in the fan, emerging at its lower end as a spring or *cinega* (Spanish for swampy ground).

Sometimes the alluvial fans at the bases of desert mountains will overlap, forming a continuous and undulating apron called a *bajada*.

Another depositional landform is the *bolson*. This is a desert basin bordered by mountains whose lower slopes are partially buried in their own debris.

Salt deposits accumulate at the end of a flowing stream where it sinks into the ground in an underground basin, or are left behind when a lake or a portion of a lake evaporates. When water temporarily fills the salt-floored basin in the desert, a playa lake is formed. (Playa lakes may also be clay-floored. When dry, clay playas make excellent landing fields.)

Alien as the desert appears to an inhabitant of more humid regions, its face has been molded by the same forces that operate all over the world. Here, as elsewhere, running water cuts the canyons and shapes the slopes. Here the wind heaps the sand into rippled dunes, just as it does many hundreds of miles away on the shores of distant seas.

Chapter 10 / The Shore and the Sea

The sea occupies almost three quarters of the surface of our planet. It was the original cradle of life and serves as the final resting place of material eroded from the land. Where sea encounters shore, wave action produces dramatic geologic changes, sometimes modifying the coast with unbelievable speed almost before our eyes.

MOVEMENTS OF THE SEA

The ocean waters move as currents, tides and waves.

Currents These are streams of moving water within the ocean, produced by solar warming, polar cooling, blowing winds and variations in salt content—all working separately or in combination. By circulating water, currents link remote regions of the world, bringing warmth to the poles and cooler water to the tropics. They also aerate (bring air to) the ocean depths.

In the North Atlantic, currents form a great whirl or eddy, circulating in a clockwise direction. A similar eddy is found in the North Pacific. In the South Atlantic and South Pacific, the currents form counterclockwise-rotating eddies.

The most conspicuous ocean currents are surface currents. A major one is the warm Gulf Stream, which actually consists of three segments traveling over thousands of miles of ocean. As it journeys through the Florida Strait, it is called the Florida Current. From Florida to the Grand Banks off Newfoundland it is called the Gulf Stream proper. As it crosses the Atlantic to Europe, it is known as the North Atlantic Current.

The Gulf Stream was described a century ago as "a

river in the sea." It is not a single river, however, but a composite of several narrow threads that constantly change position.

Huge quantities of water are transported by the Gulf Stream. It is estimated that perhaps 26 million cubic meters of water rush through the Florida Strait every second.

In the Pacific Ocean is another great current, the Japanese or Kuroshio. It travels northward, branching into the East China Sea, the Sea of Japan and the Yellow Sea. Then it drifts eastward off the coast of Japan out into the North Pacific, there mixing with the cold Oyashio Current.

The major ocean currents move far greater volumes of water than all the rivers on earth. Nevertheless, they have little significance as agents of erosion, because they move too slowly and because their energy is dissipated in friction against other water masses. Local shore currents and currents set up by the tides, however, may do considerable erosional work.

Tides Some coasts have tides that are 20 or more feet high. In other places (in much of the Mediterranean, for instance) the tides are insignificant. Typically, two high and two low tides occur within a 24-hour and 51-minute period. But elsewhere there may be only one high tide per day. The configuration of the water basin, the shape

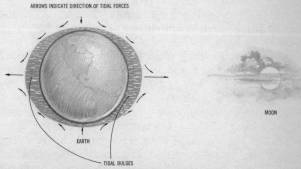

ARROWS INDICATE DIRECTION OF TIDAL FORCES

EARTH

TIDAL BULGES

MOON

High tides occur on the side of the earth nearest to the moon—where the water is pulled away from the earth—and on the side directly opposite this point—where the earth, in effect, is pulled away from the water.

of the shore and the movement of the wind affect the range and pattern of the tides. But the fundamental cause of tides is astronomical.

Tides are produced by the gravitational pull of the moon as it travels around the earth and, to a much lesser extent, by the pull of the sun. High tides occur on the side of the earth nearest the moon—where the water is pulled away from the earth—and on the side directly opposite this point—where the earth, in effect, is pulled away from the water. Low tides occur in between.

Twice each month, during the new and full moon, sun, moon and earth are aligned. Because of the added pull of the sun, the difference between high and low tides is extreme. Such extreme tides are known as spring tides.

Twice each month, when the moon is in its first and third quarters, the earth, sun and moon form a right triangle. Because the pull of the sun offsets that of the moon, the difference between high and low tides is minimal. Such sluggish tides are known as neap tides.

When tides flow through narrow channels, they produce swift and powerful currents, capable of prodigious geologic work. Tidal currents in the Bay of Fundy, between New Brunswick and Nova Scotia, sweep along at 9 miles an hour, scouring basins more than 150 feet deep. In Scotland, off the Mull of Galloway, tidal currents move coarse gravel at depths of more than 800 feet.

Waves Waves and wave currents perform a far more important role than ocean currents or tides in the shaping of the shore.

Most waves result from the friction of wind moving over water. The size and speed of waves are determined by the wind's velocity, by how long it blows from a single direction, by the depth of the water and by the fetch—the length of the open water over which it blows. Wave height (which averages 30–40 feet in storms and may be as great as 200 feet) is measured from crest to trough; wave length (which may be as much as half a mile) is measured from crest to crest or trough to trough. The time required for two successive crests or troughs to pass a given point is a wave's period, and the number of periods occurring within a given interval of time is a wave's frequency.

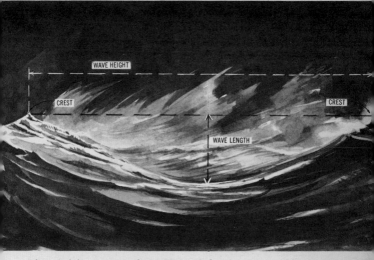

Wave heights average from 30 to 40 feet in storms and may be as great as 200 feet.

High winds blowing across the ocean can produce storm waves capable of traveling hundreds or thousands of miles from the storm area. What moves, however, is not the water of each individual wave but simply the wave *form*. As storm waves advance across the ocean, they decrease in height and increase in length, becoming smooth, rounded waves called swells. Then, as the swells approach the shore and begin to "feel bottom" at a depth equal to about half their wave length, length and velocity decrease and height increases, until the steepened crest finally topples and the wave "breaks." As these breakers collide with the coast, the shape of the shore is changed.

In deep water, a wave's energy is equally spread out all along its crest. But when a wave approaches an irregular shoreline, one part of it strikes the shallow water before the rest. As a result, the wave crest is refracted or bent and wave energy is concentrated along the headlands, dispersed along the shores of bays.

Sometimes sudden displacements of the sea floor as the result of submarine landslides, earthquakes or volcanic eruptions produce powerful waves known as tsunamis, or

seismic sea waves, or tidal waves—though they have nothing to do with tides. Although far less common than wind-made waves, tsunamis are far more destructive.

Tsunamis may travel many thousands of miles from their point of origin, eventually crashing against distant shorelines with devastating force. A dozen such waves, in 1883, were set in motion by the eruption of Krakatoa, a volcano in the East Indies. They traveled at 300–400 miles per hour, reaching South Africa, 4690 miles away, Cape Horn, 7280 miles away, and Panama, 11,470 miles away. In 1960 an earthquake in Chile sent tsunamis up to 35 feet high flashing across the Pacific. A series of waves assailed Hilo, Hawaii, 6600 miles away, where they killed 61 people and caused $20 million worth of damage.

WAVE EROSION

Wave erosion is confined to a narrow horizontal zone—perhaps 20–30 feet high on the average—between low tide and the highest point reached by storm waves.

Methods of Erosion   Waves erode the shore in three ways —by solution, by direct impact and hydraulic pressure and by abrasion.

Solution is most effective along limestone shores. Even there, however, it is a minor process.

Direct impact is considerably more effective. Moderate waves (10 feet high, 100 feet long) push against an obstruction with a pressure of 1675 pounds per square foot. Storm waves (42 feet high, 500 feet long) can exert more than 3 tons of pressure per square foot. At Wick, in northern Scotland, waves have torn away a 2600-ton concrete mass from a breakwater built to protect the harbor. Waves also compress the air in rock crevices, creating hydraulic pressures great enough to pry multi-ton blocks from cliffs. A seven-ton block from a breakwater in Ymuiden, Holland, was moved seaward because of air compression.

At the foot of many sea cliffs, in places where the rock is less resistant than elsewhere, waves hollow out sea caves.

Abrasion involves the sawing and grinding of the coast by waves laden with sand, gravel and boulders. As a rocky coast is broken up, its own fragments become additional tools with which waves erode.

Erosional Forms The most dramatic erosional form created by waves is the sea cliff (also called a wave-cut cliff). The White Cliffs of Dover, standing along the English Channel in an almost unbroken wall, are outstanding examples of sea cliffs cut from rocks offering equal resistance to erosion. Ordinarily, however, rocks vary in resistance and wave-cut cliffs form coastal patterns of protruding headlands separated by indented coves.

At the foot of many sea cliffs, in places where the rock is less resistant than elsewhere, waves hollow out sea caves, like the lovely Blue Grotto of Capri. If the landward end of a sea cave emerges at the surface, or if the roof of the cave breaks through, water may spurt out of the opening, forming blowholes or spouting horns.

As a sea cliff retreats under continual attack by waves, a flat rock surface, called a wave-cut platform or terrace, is planed off at its base, just below water level.

At many places seaward of the retreating cliffs, scattered pinnacles of erosion-resistant rock rise from the wave-cut platform. Isolated from the mainland by wave erosion, these steep-sided and chimney-like remains are known as stacks. If pierced by water they form natural bridges or arches. Stacks are found at Pte. du Van on the coast of Finisterre in northwest France, on Cannon Beach, Oregon, and in many other places. The Old Man of Hoy, off Orkney Islands on the north coast of Scotland, is a well-known stack.

Sometimes wave erosion initiates landslides by so steepening a wave-cut cliff that part of it topples into the water. Generally speaking, however, such steepening does not precipitate a landslide until heavy rains, vibrations or earthquakes set it off.

While both erosion and deposition occur on every coast, one process may drastically outrun the other. The classic example is the erosion of Heligoland in the North Sea. During the years since the ninth century, the work of the waves has reduced it from an island with 120 miles of

Huge sea stacks rise off the coast of Washington.

shoreline to an isolated rock a mere 3 miles around. Only a protective seawall has saved it from complete destruction.

Fighting Coastal Erosion   Construction of seawalls and breakwaters, however, has not always served to guard shores from violent storm waves. In most places structures called groins seem to provide better protection. Installed at right angles to the shore, these "fences" of heavy timber or concrete trap sediment, forming protective beaches at the base of cliffs.

WAVE TRANSPORTATION

The fragments of rock eroded from the shore are carried off by the ocean. The backwash of breaking waves transports eroded material out to deeper waters.

Part of the wave, however, is deflected so that it travels parallel to the shoreline as a longshore current, which may flow consistently in one direction or reverse as the wind changes. Its tendency is to move eroded materials from headlands and to deposit them in nearby bays. These currents transport huge amounts of sand along the shore.

WAVE DEPOSITION

Waves are builders as well as destroyers of the seashore. After carrying off rock fragments from the coast and grinding them down into smaller particles, they sort and deposit them.

Waves may pile up debris into gently curving crescent beaches which stretch from headland to headland. Usually a beach is composed of quartz sand, but it may also consist of boulders or of mud. When projecting points occur at close intervals, the beaches built in the small indentations between them are called pocket beaches. Bayhead beaches (or bars) accumulate in larger openings along the coast, at the head of fairly long, deep bays.

Waves often build beaches seaward, particularly when islands near a shore protect it from the full power of the sea. A famous advancing beach is Dungeness in south-eastern England, which has been growing at a rate of about 6 yards a year.

As a beach advances, it leaves behind a series of older beach ridges. These are low, rounded structures marking the landward limits of storm waves.

A ridge projecting from the shore into a body of water is called a spit. Sometimes its outer end curves to form a hook, like Sandy Hook on the New Jersey shore.

Sometimes spits grow completely, or almost completely, across a bay's entrance, forming a baymouth bar. The water enclosed by the bar and the coast is called a lagoon, which may slowly be filled with silt or sand.

Spits connecting an island with the mainland or with another island are called tombolos. Two tombolos tie Monte Argentario on the west coast of Italy to the mainland.

Longshore bars, separated by shallow troughs, run parallel to the beach. The bars form on the shallow bottom beneath the line of breakers and may be exposed at low tide.

Offshore bars or barriers, their crests showing above the water, may be built just inland from the zone of greatest breakers. Examples of offshore bars are Coney Island (New York), Atlantic City (New Jersey) and Palm Beach (Florida).

Material may also accumulate on the seaward side of wave-cut platforms, forming submarine structures called wave-built terraces.

THE SHIFTING SHORE

The relationship between the sea and shore is always shifting. Water will submerge a shoreline if the coast is lowered or the sea level raised. A shoreline will emerge from the sea if the coast is uplifted or the sea level lowered. The raising or lowering of a particular coast as the result of local earth movements is known as crustal change. The world-wide raising or lowering of the sea level, principally as the result of the expansion or contraction of continental glaciers, is known as eustatic change.

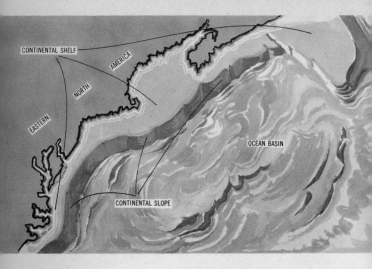

The seaward rim of each continent forms a broad, gently graded continental shelf; at the seaward end of the shelf is a sharp declivity known as the continental slope; at the foot of the slope is the ocean basin.

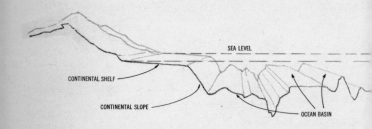

While the relative position of sea and shore are not always clear, there are certain features which indicate that water is submerging a shoreline, others which indicate that a shoreline is in the process of emerging from the sea.

Submergent Features As water inundates the land, the mouths of rivers are flooded, creating drowned river valleys. Fjords appear. At first the coast becomes more jagged, then more streamlined as headlands are eroded and spits and bars block the mouths of bays. Distinctive submergent features can be seen in this country along the south shores of Lake Erie and Lake Superior, and on the coast of Maine.

Since the Ice Age, the sea level has risen about 300 feet. As a result, most of the world's coasts show signs of submergence. Only in rare cases, when crustal movement has greatly exceeded the rise of sea level, do emergent features dominate a coast.

Emergent Features An emergent shoreline may exhibit, at dozens or hundreds of feet above sea level, features shaped by waves and currents. Formerly submerged bars and beach ridges appear. The remnant of a wave-cut platform, once under-water but now unreachable by storm waves at high tide, is still another sign that a coast is emerging. Such elevated platforms can be found on the coast of Oregon and in Peru, standing above the shoreline at the foot of the western Andes.

THE FLOOR OF THE SEA

The Continental Shelf Beyond the shore, the rim of each continent angles seaward, forming a broad, gently graded continental shelf. Off some coasts, like the Mediterranean and parts of Indonesia, this shelf is so small it is virtually not there. On the northern coast of Siberia, on the other hand, it is about 750 miles wide.

In the recent geologic past, the shallower parts of the continental shelves were dry, providing land bridges from India to Ceylon, from Siberia to the New World. Many terrestrial features still remain, like glacier-formed drumlins and terminal moraines.

The Continental Slope   The seaward margins of the continental shelves are marked by an abrupt increase in steepness. This sharp declivity is known as the continental slope.

Cut into the continental slope in many places are mysterious steep-walled canyons, some the size of the Grand Canyon of the Colorado. Among the great submarine canyons are the Monterey Canyon off California, the Congo Canyon and the Nazare Canyon off Portugal. Their origin is the subject of much debate, but a favorite hypothesis credits turbidity currents. These are streams of dense, muddy water which may exist in the sea, excavating canyons as they roll down the continental slope and then spreading out broad expanses of sediment across the abyss.

The Abyss   This is the stretch of ocean floor that sprawls from one continental margin to another at the foot of the continental slopes. The abyss was once believed to be a featureless plain. But after World War I, oceanographers discovered that our seascape displays not only abyssal plains but under-water scenery as diversified as any seen on land.

There are broad rises and plateaus with gentle slopes, and steeper-sloped ridges with narrow crests. Some of these ridges form awesome mountain ranges. The Mid-Atlantic Ridge, for instance, extends for 10,000 miles down the full length of the ocean, midway between the continents. The tall peaks of this submarine mountain range poke up through the surface of the sea and serve as the foundations of such islands as Ascension, the Azores, Iceland, St. Helena and Tristan da Cunha.

Rising above the abyssal plains are isolated, individual peaks called seamounts, which are, possibly, submarine volcanoes. Also present are guyots—little mountains with mysterious flat-topped summits. Seamounts are plentiful in the Gulf of Alaska. Numerous guyots are found between the Hawaiian and Mariana Islands.

Many depressions cut below the surface of the ocean floor. Some are rounded basins, some elongated troughs with gently sloping sides, some steep-walled trenches. Depressions with floors below 23,000 feet are known as deeps. Among the champion deeps are the Mindanao Trench off the Philippines (34,428 feet), the Mariana

Trench near Guam (35,800 feet) and the Vityaz Deep off the Kurile Islands (34,000 feet).

A crucial difference between seascapes and landscapes is the absence, below the sea, of familiar erosional processes. Although rock falls and landslides occur, there are no blowing winds, pouring rains or glacial rasp to modify the ocean scenery.

MARINE DEPOSITS

Sediments can be found on the continental shelves, the continental slopes and the deep-sea floor. Most of the sediment laid down in the sea is derived from the erosion of the land and from the remains of marine animals and plants. Other sources are submarine volcanoes and a small amount of meteoritic dust.

Clay, silt, sand and mud cover the shelves and slopes. About 60% of the continental slope, it has been estimated, is mud—probably bluish or greenish in color.

There are three main types of deep-sea deposits—calcareous ooze (covering about 48% of the floor), red clay (covering 38%) and siliceous ooze (covering 14%).

Ooze is an ivory-colored powdery blanket composed of the shells and tests of free-floating organisms sifting ceaselessly down from the surface. The most abundant components of calcareous ooze are the shells of *Foraminifera* and the plates of calcareous algae. Siliceous ooze is chiefly the tiny remains of the beautifully ornamental *Radiolaria,* found in an equatorial strip across the eastern Pacific, and the prolific diatom, a single-celled, surface-dwelling plant of the cold water.

Red clay is chiefly quartz, mica and a variety of clay minerals, usually stained red by iron rust. It covers most of the very deep ocean floor with a monotonous soft carpet of extremely fine-grained, deep reddish-brown particles. These particles are carried from the land to the sea by rivers, waves or wind and purveyed far and wide by ocean currents, eventually sifting down to the bottom of the sea.

Lumpy masses of manganese dioxide—up to 3 inches in diameter—are strange deposits which form by accretion on some parts of the deep-sea floor. How these deposits accumulate is unclear, but it is thought that they are chemically precipitated.

In addition to these deposits, there are broad, fan-shaped expanses of sand, bedded with the coarser layers at the base and the finer at top. These are spread across the abyssal plains where, ordinarily, ooze would occur, and are believed to have been deposited by turbidity currents. Often they contain the remains of organisms living in the shallow waters near the margins of the ocean basin.

CORAL REEFS

One of the most beautiful and interesting deposits of shore and sea is the coral reef, built of living coral and the skeletons of those that have died. Algae and a number of other calcareous organisms contribute importantly to the formation of the reef, but corals provide the conspicuous framework.

Corals are members of the phylum Coelenterata, a group of spineless animals that include sea anemones and jellyfish. After anchoring themselves firmly to a foundation, corals take calcium carbonate out of the water and build of it a limy exterior to enclose their fragile jelly-like bodies. When the corals die, their shells remain part of the reef, serving as a foundation upon which live corals build their structure upward.

Corals form large colonies of tightly interlocked individuals. They require for their survival and development warm water whose temperature remains above 68° F, preferably between 77° and 86° F. This water must be clear, normally saline and constantly stirred. It must also be fairly shallow—no deeper than 150 feet—so that there is enough sunlight for the photosynthesis necessary to the microscopic algae with which corals live interdependently. The waters that best meet these conditions are found in the Pacific and Indian Oceans, but some corals also occur in the Atlantic Ocean and the Red Sea.

There are three major reef forms—fringing reefs, barrier reefs and atolls.

A fringing reef is a belt of coral built along the border of the shore. Most are under 100 feet wide, but a few measure in the thousands.

A barrier reef is separated from the shore by a lagoon or channel. The outstanding example is the Great Barrier Reef of Australia, stretching for 1260 miles at distances ranging from 25 to nearly 200 miles offshore.

An atoll is a ring-like reef enclosing a central lagoon. There are, according to one study, about 330 atolls in the tropical seas of the world, almost all in the Indian and Pacific Oceans. Most are small, but there are some exceptions—Kwajelein in the Marshall Islands of the South Pacific is 75 miles long and in some places averages 15 miles across.

More than a century ago Charles Darwin proposed the theory that there is a natural sequence to coral reefs. If an island with a fringing reef subsided slowly, he said, the reef would subside too, but at the same time it would grow upward. As the edges of the island sunk, the reef would become a barrier reef. Later, as subsidence continued and the entire central island drowned, the barrier reef would become an atoll. Although this theory has been modified in many ways since Darwin's time, it is still an important contribution to the study of coral-reef development.

Chapter 11 / Vulcanism and Volcanoes

Erosion . . . transportation . . . deposition. These words have occurred again and again in the preceding chapters to describe the major external geologic processes. This chapter will look at a major internal geologic process—vulcanism.

Vulcanism involves the activities of magma—molten material below the surface of the earth—and lava—magma that has reached the earth's surface through cracks and fissures. Vulcanism is responsible for the presence of all igneous rocks (the primary rocks of the earth, discussed in Chapter 4) and for certain unique types of rock structures (such as batholiths, dikes and sills). The most dramatic instances of vulcanism, of course, are volcanoes, whose fiery eruptions reveal the seething liquid that forms beneath the earth's rocky face.

MAGMA

Magma is a very complex, high-temperature solution of silicates containing water and other gases. It originates in the earth's crust or upper mantle as a result of local melting of solid rock. At these depths rock temperatures are so high that they can maintain their solid state only because of the immense pressure exerted by the overlying rock. If pressure is reduced, the rock changes into liquid in a local magma chamber.

Lighter and more mobile than solid rock, magma tends to work its way upward to the surface. Sometimes the pressure of neighboring rocks squeezes magma through pre-existing fissures, zones of weakness and regions of lessened pressure. Sometimes magma moves, so to speak, under its own steam—either by melting the overlying rocks or forcing them aside. Magma may begin with temperatures in the 1000°–2000° range but will eventually cool. Anywhere along its upward course it may solidify.

Magma which has "intruded" into the older overlying and surrounding rock of the earth's crust and then solidified forms what are called intrusive igneous rocks. Igneous rocks are called extrusive if they form from cooling lava at earth's surface.

INTRUSIVE IGNEOUS BODIES

Although intrusive rocks were formed at depth, we can see them now at the surface of the earth because the overlying rock has been eroded. There are several distinct types of intrusive igneous bodies.

Batholiths These great bodies of granite and granodiorite are the largest intrusive igneous bodies, with an exposed surface area of more than 40 square miles. Indirect evidence indicates that batholiths taper downward, but no one has ever seen a batholith floor. As a result, geologists

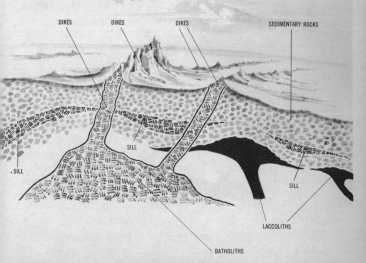

Magma which has "intruded" into the older rocks of the earth's crust and then solidified forms "intrusive igneous bodies" such as batholiths, dikes, sills, and laccoliths.

are uncertain of the batholith's shape, but it has been described as "circular, elliptical, or quite irregular."

Batholiths extend along the cores of most major mountain ranges and underlie vast segments of the ancient shields—large areas where igneous rocks outcrop at the surface. The batholith in the Coast Range of British Columbia is at least 1000 miles long and 20–150 miles wide.

Stocks   A batholith whose exposed surface area is less than 40 square miles is called a stock. Examples are the Spanish Peaks, unusually symmetrical twin stocks found in southern Colorado.

Dikes   While batholiths are deep-seated intrusions, dikes and other smaller intrusive bodies occur at intermediate depths. A dike is a flat, tabular, commonly basaltic formation with two of its three dimensions much larger than the third. It is discordant, which means that it cuts across the layering of the rocks it invades.

Dikes range in thickness from a few inches to over 100 feet. Some are hundreds of miles long. The length of the Great Dike of Rhodesia, for instance, exceeds 300 miles.

Dikes usually occur in groups called dike swarms. Sometimes dikes have a parallel arrangement; sometimes they radiate outward from a volcano. When the overlying rock is eroded, dikes may appear on the surface of the earth as prominent ridges.

Sills   Like dikes, sills have a tabular shape, differ greatly in size and are often found in swarms. The key difference between them is that sills, unlike dikes and most other intrusive bodies, are concordant—they lie parallel to the enclosing rock layers whether those rocks are horizontal or tilted vertically. A sill is fairly flat, like a sedimentary bed, and is most commonly composed of dolerite. Examples are the Great Whin Sill in Northumberland (northeastern England) and the Palisades, an abrupt cliff which follows the Hudson along the New Jersey shore.

Laccoliths   These sill-like formations have a flat base and a convex upper surface. They occur when magma "piles up" between sedimentary layers and forces the overlying

Paricutin, the volcano that arose 200 miles west of Mexico City, is shown before its eruptions tore into its side and broke the top cone.

rock into a dome or arch shape. Laccoliths, rarely more than a few miles across, are composed of the same materials as dikes and sills and, like them, tend to form clusters. The Henry Mountains in Utah are the classic example of laccoliths.

Volcanic Necks Also called volcanic plugs, these are vertical, pipe-like, cylindrical bodies of igneous rock which fill the throats of volcanoes and through which lava rises. Because they are composed of more resistant material than volcanoes—usually porphyritic rock—they are left standing high on the landscape long after the volcanoes themselves have been eroded away.

A well-known volcanic neck, found in New Mexico, is Ship Rock, which rises more than 1300 feet above the plateau. Altogether, more than 150 volcanic necks stand as steep-sided buttes above the plateaus of northwestern New Mexico and Arizona. Another fascinating group of volcanic necks are the pipes of kimberlite, a source of diamonds in South Africa.

VOLCANOES

The word volcano originates from the island Vulcano, situated in the Mediterranean Sea. It was once believed that the hot lava fragments erupting from Vulcano flew from the forge of the Roman fire god Vulcan as he fashioned thunderbolts for Jupiter and arrows for Diana.

Rituals related to fire deities occurred among many people who dwelt in lands of volcanoes—the Aztecs of Mexico, the Polynesians of the Pacific, the Japanese of Honshu. Even in modern times, in modern Hawaii, gifts of breadfruit and pork have been offered to the mythical Pele, goddess of volcanoes.

Scientists, however, have made great advances in their understanding of volcanoes, and the facts they have assembled are steadily replacing supernatural explanations. They have defined and categorized volcanoes and determined where they are located. They have also documented some of the great volcanic eruptions in recent earth history.

Definition of Volcano A volcano is, ordinarily, a conical mountain or hill from which are liberated, through a central vent or through side vents, liquid lava, pyroclastic debris and gases.

Lava is magma that does not solidify below ground, reaching the surface still fluid and molten but minus a large portion of its gases (mostly steam) and its liquids (mostly water). Lava is red-hot when it pours from the vent but turns dark red, gray or black as it cools to extrusive igneous rock.

Pyroclastic debris—pellets of molten lava, chunks of already consolidated lava and fragments of older rocks— form another group of extrusive igneous rocks. The finest particles are called volcanic ash and dust. Intermediate-size pieces are called cinders or lapilli. Larger fragments are called volcanic blocks if they were angular solids at the time of ejection, volcanic bombs if they were ejected in a liquid state and subsequently solidified in flight into rounded or spindle shapes.

The gases include a high proportion of steam, as well as carbon dioxide and compounds of sulfur, chlorine, fluorine and boron. Gases are responsible for the vehemence of explosive volcanic eruptions. Expanding gases escape easily from the fluid basaltic lavas but are trapped for a longer time in the highly viscous lavas such as rhyolite. When they finally burst forth, they do so with great explosive force.

Distribution of Volcanoes About 500 active volcanoes (those that have erupted at least once in recorded history) exist on earth. Many of the world's tallest peaks are large volcanoes. Many well-known islands are the summits of volcanoes rising from the floor of the sea.

Volcanoes do not appear as a random scattering, but are concentrated within certain well-defined bands which roughly resemble the distribution of earthquakes. Most volcanoes seem to be located where actively growing mountain ranges are concentrated. Most are near the sea. And most volcanoes appear where there is fracturing in the earth's crust, fractures along which magma might travel to reach the surface.

The most striking volcanic band is the so-called "ring of fire" that borders the Pacific Ocean. From Tierra del Fuego, the belt extends through the Andes region, along the western coast of Central America and into Mexico. The belt continues from Mexico through the Cascade Ranges to Alaska, then through the Aleutian Islands to Kamchatka. From there it goes to Japan, the Philippines, the East Indies and New Zealand.

There is no comparable volcanic belt along the margins of the Atlantic. The Lesser Antilles (West Indies), however, is a volcanic island arc system (a curved line of small islands) separating the Caribbean Sea from the Atlantic Ocean. A famous volcano of this area is Mount Pelée.

Another volcanic belt stretches from the Mediterranean through Asia Minor to the East Indies archipelago. Famous Mediterranean volcanoes include Vulcano, Vesuvius, Etna and Stromboli.

Volcanoes also rise from the floors of the Pacific, Indian and Atlantic Oceans. Those in the Atlantic occur along the Mid-Atlantic Ridge, forming the islands of the Azores, Cape Verde Islands, St. Paul's Rocks and Iceland. The Hawaiian Islands are Mid-Pacific volcanoes. In the Indian Ocean is the notorious Indonesian volcano Krakatoa.

A few active volcanoes are located in the interior of the continents, particularly in central and eastern Africa. The most notable is the snow-crested Kilimanjaro.

Classification of Volcanoes   Unlike the mountains that will be discussed in Chapter 13, volcanic mountains are built by the accumulation of their own eruptive products. Volcanoes are classified according to the shape and composition of their cones. ·

Cinder cones are heaped-up piles of pyroclastic materials blown out in explosive eruptions. These steep-sided cones may have 25°–30° slopes, but rarely rise more than 1000 feet above their surroundings. They are very numerous in western North America, and include Sunset Crater of Arizona. Mexico's Parícutin, born in 1943, is also a cinder-cone volcano.

Shield volcanoes are built up gradually by successive overlapping and coalescing lava flows. They have a broad, near-circular outline and a gently rounded profile, with slopes that rarely exceed 10° Some of our biggest volcanoes are shield volcanoes. The Hawaiian Islands are composed of clusters of them, including the world's largest active volcano, Mauna Loa, which stands 13,680 feet above sea level and more than 15,000 feet below, thus achieving a total height of almost 30,000 feet.

Lava domes may form steep-sided craggy knobs or spines over the volcanic vent, or short, steep-sided lava flows known as coulees. Such volcanoes are composed of very viscous or pasty lava. An example is Mount Pelée in Martinique, whose domes developed in the course of the most destructive eruption known to mankind. California's Lassen Peak is another lava dome.

Composite cones, also called strato-volcanoes, have alternating layers of lava and pyroclastic materials because eruptions in the life history of such volcanoes include both the relatively quiet outpourings of lava and the violent explosions of ash, cinders, bombs and blocks. Such volcanic mountains are steeper than shield volcanoes but not as steep as cinder cones. Many are 6000–8000 feet high. Composite cones include snow-capped Fujiyama in Japan, Vesuvius in Italy, Mount Hood in Oregon and Cotopaxi in Ecuador.

Sometimes lava or pyroclastic debris emerges from fissures in a volcano's weakened sides, rather than through its central vent. Cones formed in this way, on the flanks of the main volcano, are called parasitic cones.

A volcano's central vent occupies a funnel-shaped depression called a crater. Sometimes, as a result of the collapse or explosion of a cone, this crater enlarges, becoming a basin known as a caldera. Oregon's splendid Crater Lake, nearly 2000 feet deep in places, fills a caldera 6 miles in diameter.

Eruptions of Volcanoes According to one study, there have been some 2500 volcanic eruptions since the beginning of recorded history. Close to 2000 of these occurred in the Pacific Basin. The eruptions can be broadly classified as explosive, intermediate, quiet and fissure. Heavy flows of lava tend to accompany quiet and fissure eruptions, while the expulsion of great quantities of pyroclastic debris is associated with explosive eruptions.

Explosive eruptions are impressively exemplified by the titanic explosions which rocked the Indonesian island of Krakatoa. This volcanic island, standing between Java and Sumatra in the Sunda Straits, was originally formed when three composite cones of lava and pyroclastic fragments grew up from the sea floor and coalesced into one large island with three summits. Then, in August 1883, Krakatoa erupted in a series of blasts heard nearly 3000 miles away.

Some 5 cubic miles of material were blown into the air and a cloud of volcanic ash rose to heights of about 50 miles. The finer particles remained suspended in the air for years, causing brilliant sunsets in much of the world. The eruption of Krakatoa also set into motion one of the most destructive seismic sea waves in recorded history, which killed some 30,000–40,000 people on the low-lying shores of Java and Sumatra.

When the explosion subsided, about two-thirds of the island had vanished. In its place was a caldera, its floor 1000 feet below sea level, its bowl-shaped depression filled with ocean water. It is believed that the caldera was formed not by the explosion of the volcanic cone but by the cone's collapse. In like manner, it is hypothesized, Oregon's Crater Lake originated after the eruption and collapse of a volcanic mountain which has been named Mount Mazama.

After a quiet period in Krakatoa's history, eruptions constructed a new volcanic cone on the floor of the caldera in 1927. It is called Anak Krakatoa (child of Krakatoa) and its summit now rises above the sea.

Another classic explosive eruption was that of Mount Pelée in May 1902. The explosion of this lava dome, situated on the island of Martinique in the West Indies, destroyed the entire city of St. Pierre and some 30,000 people —all but two of its inhabitants. One of the survivors was inexplicably lucky—though severely burned, he came out of the disaster alive. The other survivor was protected by his environment—the poorly ventilated underground dungeon in which he had been incarcerated on a charge of murder.

When Mount Pelée exploded, it expelled great, dense, glowing clouds of superheated steam and red-hot dust and

Intermediate eruptions are typified by the renowned Vesuvius, near Naples, Italy.

ash which swept down the mountainside like an avalanche at more than 60 miles per hour. One of these burning avalanches rolled fatally over the hapless St. Pierre.

Vulcanologists studying these glowing clouds have termed them *nuées ardentes*. They are formed, it has been learned, by the violent explosions of viscous lava, but are not ordinarily accompanied by thinner, more fluid lava flows. The *nuée ardente* that murdered St. Pierre had a temperature of 650°–700° C.

By October 1902 the ejection of *nuées ardentes* had just about ceased, and a plug had formed in the volcano's throat. This plug, pushed upward by the vast power of the volcano's confined, high-temperature gases, formed a stiff spire of hardened lava which grew more than 1000 feet above the crater floor, after which it gradually disintegrated.

Pelée erupted again in 1929, with a series of *nuées ardentes* that continued for three years. The eruptions ended when the vent was sealed by a dome of solid lava.

Since 1932 Pelée has been dormant. No one knows, at this stage, whether the volcano's fires are banked or whether it will erupt again with clouds of incandescent death.

Intermediate eruptions are typified by the renowned Vesuvius, near Naples, Italy, and the volcanic island Stromboli, which rises abruptly from the sea north of Sicily.

Vesuvius, the only active volcano on the mainland of Europe, erupted into history in A.D. 79, killing 20,000 people. The eruptions buried the city of Pompeii beneath 15–25 feet of volcanic ash and choked the city of Herculaneum with a volcanic mudflow—a swift-moving mass of ash, cinders, pumice and lava fragments washed by rain from the volcano's upper slopes.

During the eruption, Pliny the Elder lost his life while directing the evacuation of refugees. An eye-witness account of the eruption was reported by Pliny the Younger.

The subsequent history of Vesuvius has been: (1) repeated explosive eruptions at intervals of 50–100 years; followed by (2) a period of almost complete repose between 1139 and 1631; (3) destructive eruptions in December 1631; (4) continuous activity involving both lava flows and pyroclastic debris; (5) a long (since 1944) phase of repose which may be the beginning of centuries of dormancy or the lull before another catastrophic eruption.

Stromboli, one of the world's largest volcanoes, begins 7000 feet below sea level and rises from the sea for 3000 more. An almost perfect twin-peaked cone, it is called "the lighthouse of the Mediterranean" because it has been moderately active for more than 2000 years.

Gas and steam continuously escape from vents in its crater. There are frequent minor explosions of pyroclastic debris. And, occasionally, the volcano emits small outpourings of lava, which prevent the storing of enough energy to produce violent eruptions. As with Vesuvius, the ejection of both ash and lava builds a composite cone.

Quiet (or Hawaiian) eruptions involve an enormous outpouring of basaltic lava, sometimes accompanied by lava fountains 1000 feet high. This lava is far more fluid than the viscous lava typical of Vesuvian-type eruptions and so the associated gases are liberated without much explosive violence. Such eruptions produce shield volcanoes.

The island of Hawaii is the upper part of five consolidated shield volcanoes. Only two of them—the towering Mauna Loa and the considerably lower Kilauea—are currently active.

Mauna Loa has been built by thousands of individual lava flows, averaging about 10 feet thick, which have intermittently erupted from its summit crater and from fissures on its sides since 1832. The longest recorded eruption began on April 20, 1873, and lasted about 1½ years.

In a typical eruption one or more fissures, several miles long, open up and several geyser-like fountains squirt from them, increasing in intensity. A yellow-brown gas cloud rises several thousand feet above the fountains, while lava pours out and flows down the volcano's sides. The fountains halt, a short period of lava outpouring follows and the eruption ends.

Kilauea, only about 4000 feet above sea level, rises from Mauna Loa's southeastern slope. Most of its activity is confined to only part of its caldera, a firepit called Halemaumau, whose lava occasionally rises and floods the crater.

Both the molten lava and the solid rock it forms are known as lava flows. Hardened lava flows are the most common extrusive igneous rock.

Hawaiians distinguish between two kinds of lava. The "aa" has a rough, jagged, blocky appearance. The "pahoehoe" is smoother and more undulating, with twisted rope-like wrinkles covering its surface. In addition, there is a pillowy surface marked by irregular curved cracks, indicating that the lava cooled under water.

Pele's hair, which rains down on the neighboring regions during the lava-fountain stage, is an unusual feature of Hawaiian eruptions. Pele's hair is natural spun glass, a hair-like substance produced by the action of the wind on the exposed lava.

Fissure eruptions may occur on the sides of volcanoes but the presence of volcanoes is not essential for this type of eruption. Sometimes lava pours out of extensive cracks in the earth's surface, cracks that are in no way connected with volcanic cones.

Such successive fissure eruptions have built up great basaltic plateaus in several parts of the world. An outstanding example is the Columbia Plateau of the American Northwest, with a surface of 200,000 square miles and a volume of about 75,000 cubic miles. The basalt that formed this plateau reached the surface through hundreds, perhaps thousands of fissures.

Other great plateaus are India's Deccan Plateau and the Parana Basin of South America.

SECONDARY VOLCANIC PHENOMENA

Geysers and hot springs are usually found in regions of volcanic activity. Also associated with volcanoes are fumeroles—openings in the earth's crust from which steam and other gases of magmatic origin escape.

But none of these can perform with the flamboyant style of an erupting volcano. With its great, sinister clouds of steam and ash boiling upward, its fleet incandescent bombs streaking through the sky and its molten lava streaming implacably down the cone, it is a powerful reminder of the forces within our earth.

Chapter 12 / Diastrophism and Earthquakes

When plateaus are pushed upward, when large segments of crust sink downward, when great mountain ranges appear on the earth, diastrophism is at work. Like vulcanism, diastrophism is an internal geologic process. It involves all movements of the solid parts of the earth and is responsible for the geologic structures resulting from these movements, whether they appear at the surface or below it, and whether they occur on a large or tiny scale.

Evidence of diastrophism is the startling presence, high on Everest's slopes, of water-laid rock containing fossils of sea-dwelling organisms that lived 60 million years ago. Also evidence of diastrophism is the sudden, devastating wrench of a major earthquake.

TYPES OF EARTH MOVEMENTS

Major earthquakes are produced by sudden movements of the earth. Most earth movements, however, are slow and slight. Yet even at the rate of a handful of inches per century, repeated earth movements have time enough to produce changes eventually measurable in thousands of feet.

Vertical earth movements may alter the relationship between land and sea by raising or lowering the coast. The earth also moves horizontally, compressing the rocks as if they were squeezed in an enormous vise.

A classic example of the rising (uplift) and lowering (subsidence) of the land is the Temple of Jupiter Serapis, an ancient Roman ruin on a seashore near Naples. The ruin displays three columns, each circled with a line about 23 feet above sea level. Below this line, within a 9-foot-wide band, each column is bored full of holes of shallow-water shellfish. The appearance of the columns indicates that the dry land on which the temple was built subsided (as the result of slow downward movements), then rose (as the result of slow upward movements) in the years since its construction in the second century B.C.

Both horizontal and vertical earth movements are responsible for the two basic structural forms of diastrophism—folds and faults. (Folds tend to be related to horizontal movements; faults to vertical ones.)

Folds occur when rock is deformed by bending, so that the original position of the layers of bedrock is changed, but the beds are still continuous. Faults occur when there is a break in the rock, accompanied by displacement along the plane of the fracture surface. Folds and faults are most common in the rocks of mountain ranges (to be discussed in the following chapter) but can be observed there only imperfectly, for erosion quickly obscures the original forms.

All types of rocks may fold or fault. But these occurrences are most easily observed in sedimentary rocks, because their distinctive bedding planes provide clues to the nature and extent of earth movements.

WARPING

Rocks in the earth's crust are generally regarded as solid. But they are, actually, somewhat plastic. If weakened by high temperature and subjected to great pressure they will become deformed. Slight deformation on a large scale is called warping.

Broadly speaking, warping refers to the continental-scale vertical movements that lift extensive plateaus and maintain earth's isostatic balance. Local warping contributes to the uplift and subsidence of a coastal area.

FOLDING

Folding is like warping but involves a greater degree of deformation. Most folds are produced by horizontal movements in the earth.

Attitude of Folds   As a rule, sedimentary rocks are deposited as horizontal layers. When these layers are

Folds occur when rock is deformed by bending; most are produced by horizontal movements of the earth.

strongly tilted, or vertical, they have been deformed. The attitude, or position, of sedimentary rocks is defined by geologists in terms of two concepts—dip and strike.

Layered rocks deposited horizontally have an inclination of 0°. If subsequently tilted until vertical, they have an inclination, or dip, of 90°. Thus the angle of a rock layer's deviation from a horizontal plane is the rock's dip.

Where a dipping rock layer intersects the surface of the earth, it is seen as a line running across country. The direction of this line is called the strike, and is recorded as a direction—north, southwest, etc.

Kinds of Folds Upfolds, or arches, in rocks are called anticlines, and resemble the crests of waves. Downfolds in rocks are called synclines, and resemble the troughs in waves. A monocline is a flexure in a series of beds which are nearly horizontal on either side of the flexure.

It is important to remember that anticlines are not always mountains nor are synclines always valleys. If a downfold is made of more erosion-resistant rock than its adjacent upfold, it will eventually form a mountain summit while its neighbor is reduced to a lowland by erosion.

The two sides of an anticline or syncline are called limbs. They are sometimes identical, forming a symmetrical fold, but more frequently one limb will be steeper than the other, resulting in an asymmetrical fold. If the beds in the lower limb of an anticline have been tilted beyond the vertical, so that both limbs dip in the same direction with one doubled beneath the other, the result is an overturned fold. A recumbent fold is one that has been forced over on its side so that it is virtually horizontal. An open fold is less compressed than a closed fold. When the limbs of folds are parallel, dipping in the same direction, a fold is isoclinal. An isoclinal fold may be upright, overturned or recumbent. When a fold dies out, that is, disappears or "plunges" underground, it is known as a plunging fold.

Anticlines and synclines sometimes form structural domes and basins. A structural dome is produced by an anticline dipping outward from a central area. A structural basin is built when a syncline dips in a circular pattern toward a common center.

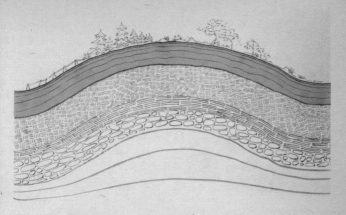

When the two sides, or limbs, of an anticline
are identical they form a symmetrical fold.

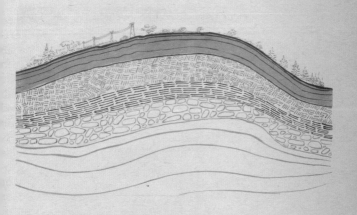

When one limb of an anticline is steeper than
the other, an asymmetrical fold is formed.

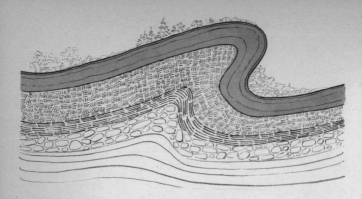

If the beds in the lower limb of an anticline have been tilted beyond the vertical, so that both limbs dip in the same direction with one doubled beneath the other, the result is an overturned fold.

OPPOSITE: Any crack in solid rock is a fracture; when a fracture is accompanied by movement of the rocks a fault is produced.

An oblique-slip fault involves approximately equal vertical and horizontal movements.

A dip-slip fault involves vertical movement. When the rocks above the fracture move down with respect to those below the fracture, the dip slip is called a normal fault.

When the rocks above the fracture move up with respect to those below, the dip slip is called a thrust fault.

A recumbent fold is one that has been forced over on its side so that it is virtually horizontal.

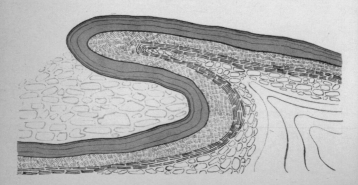

A strike-slip fault is a fracture along which
movement has been predominantly horizontal.

FAULTING

Any crack in solid rock is a fracture. An open fracture,
which may serve as a channel for lava, is a fissure. Fractures along which there has been no significant movement,
occurring in parallel groups, are called joints.

When a fracture or fissure is accompanied by movement of the rocks on either side, a fault is produced. (The
actual break is called the fault plane.) Rocks may be displaced only a fraction of an inch. But sometimes the movements of rocks along a fault plane may add up to hundreds
of miles.

Classification of Faults   The direction of apparent movement along a fault fracture is the basis on which faults are
classified.

A dip-slip fault is a fracture along which movement
has been predominantly vertical.

A strike-slip fault is a fracture along which movement
has been predominantly horizontal.

An oblique-slip fault involves approximately equal
vertical and horizontal movements.

In almost all dip-slip faults the fracture surface is not
literally vertical. Instead, the fracture has a decided dip

and the rocks slip along it. The direction of movement may be up or down. When the rocks above the fracture move down with respect to those below the fracture, we have a normal fault. When the rocks above the fracture move up with respect to those below, we have a thrust fault. A steep thrust fault, involving angles of more than 45°, is called a reverse fault.

Strike-slip faults, which involve horizontal movement, are also known as lateral faults. A lateral fault may be right lateral or left lateral, depending on the direction of the displacement.

Fault Displacement   No single observed fault movement in history has been great enough to explain marine shells in the rocks of tall mountains. It is the recurrent growth of a fault, as it is broken and broken again by abrupt earthquakes or slow continuous movements, that eventually produces a major displacement.

Vertical displacement of rocks may result in block mountains (to be discussed in the following chapter), fault scarps, horsts, grabens or rift valleys.

A fault scarp is a low, linear cliff on the upthrown side of a fault—the side where the block of rocks seems to have moved up.

A single elongated block, uplifted between two normal faults, forms a plateau called a horst.

A graben is an elongated crustal block that has been lowered between two normal faults, forming a trench or trough bounded by fault scarps. The Rhine Graben is an example.

A rift valley is a continuous line of grabens, like the one extending through Africa and part of the Middle East from Mozambique to the Dead Sea.

EARTHQUAKES

One of the most notable—and catastrophic—consequences of faulting is the earthquake. An earthquake is a natural vibration of the ground produced by the rupturing of large masses of rock beneath the surface.

Causes of Earthquakes   Sometimes minor earthquakes occur as a result of volcanic eruptions, avalanches, explosions or the collapse of underground caverns. But all really significant earthquakes are tectonic. That is, they are due to movements within the solid earth—specifically the abrupt slippage of rock masses along a fault, even when no visible movement along the fault is discernible at the surface.

Although such movements release prodigious amounts of energy suddenly, this energy, according to the widely accepted elastic-rebound theory, has probably been accumulating for a very long time. Slow movements along the fault build up strains in the rocks on both sides, like the strain that is built up in a stretched rubber band. But like the rubber band, which will stretch only so far and then break, the rocks have a limit to their elasticity. Strained beyond that limit, they will suddenly rupture and rebound, releasing their stored-up energy as earthquake waves.

Sometimes some breaking occurs before the principal shock. These are known as foreshocks. Sometimes there are adjustments along the fault zone after the principal shock. These are known as aftershocks.

Most of the strain in the rocks, however, is released when the principal shock takes place. Thereafter, the ruptured zone will remain a plane of weakness, and further abrupt movements along faults will recur when stresses build up again.

Distribution of Earthquakes Although, in theory, no place on earth is completely safe from earthquakes, most major quakes take place where active volcanoes are located. About 80%–90% of the shallow and intermediate shocks, and almost all the deep-focus quakes, are concentrated around the borders of the Pacific Ocean. Others occur in a belt extending from the Mediterranean through Asia; in the Mid-Atlantic and Mid-Indian Ridges; and in the Hawaiian Islands and African rift valleys.

Of the industrial nations, Japan is subjected to the most frequent and intense earthquakes. Other key areas are Indonesia, New Zealand, the Philippines and the west coasts of North and South America. The California-Nevada region has had about 5000 quakes a year since the first one was recorded in 1769.

Classification of Earthquakes The place below the surface where the quake originates is called the focus. The place on earth's surface immediately above the focus is called the epicenter. Earthquakes may be shallow, intermediate or deep, depending on the depth of their foci.

Shallow earthquakes, which have the greatest energy and are the most numerous, originate within 40 miles of the surface.

Intermediate earthquakes have foci between 40 and 200 miles down.

Deep-focus earthquakes generally originate at depths between 200 and 400 miles, though the deepest recorded is 435 miles. Deep-focus earthquakes are often of great magnitude, but they can be felt over large areas without doing serious damage.

Effects of Earthquakes Although earthquakes are of only minor importance as geologic agents, they have major effects on people and property. At their most destructive, they are responsible for ruined cities, raging fires and floods, deaths by the tens of thousands. Fissures often open in the ground, landslides and avalanches are set in motion, icebergs and glaciers are shaken loose. Large areas of land may be uplifted or depressed. Rivers may rise or fall, or even run upstream.

Earthquakes also cause seismic sea waves or tsunamis, which can be as high as a record 210 feet and which travel across the ocean at high speeds, thousands of miles from their point of origin (see pp. 121, 140). These gigantic waves have, on occasion, been more destructive than the quake that engendered them. Upon reaching shore, a tsunami may first produce a dramatic withdrawal of the water. But within a few minutes the wave rushes in at high speeds, smashing everything in its path.

As a rule, destruction is more severe nearer the epicenter than farther away. Buildings on filled, water-soaked or unconsolidated ground are more badly damaged than those on solid rock or dry, well-consolidated soil. Buildings that are not too rigid and are designed to vibrate as a single unit seem to be best able to survive the shock.

The exact time, place and magnitude of earthquakes

cannot yet be predicted with reasonable accuracy. Of the million or so quakes which occur each year, at least 20 or 30 are of great magnitude, capable of causing major catastrophes. Fortunately, most of these earthquakes originate below the sea—far away from land—or in sparsely populated mountain areas. Still, disasters have occurred on the average of one every two or three years during the last three centuries.

Earthquake Waves   The energy released when rocks move along a fault plane is transmitted away from the focus as earthquake waves. Those that follow paths within the earth are called body waves. Those that follow paths in the outer crust of the earth are called surface or long (L) waves.

L waves travel more slowly than body waves. They are the ones felt by people at the surface of the earth, and the ones that destroy life and property.

Body waves are of two main types: there are P waves, also called primary, push, pressure, compressional or longitudinal waves; and there are S waves, also called secondary, shake, shear, distortional or transverse waves.

In P waves, each rock particle vibrates to and fro in the direction in which the wave is traveling. Primary waves can travel through solids, liquids and gases.

In S waves, the particles vibrate at right angles to the direction in which the wave is traveling. S waves can only travel through solid bodies.

The velocity of P waves is almost double that of S waves. The velocity of both increases with depth to about 1800 miles and then decreases.

The behavior patterns of P and S waves as they pass through the earth have provided important information about the lithosphere (see Chapter 2, p. 12). Through them we have developed the concept of a layered earth with a crust, mantle and core, and have begun to determine the nature of the materials which comprise these layers.

Seismographs and Seismograms   A seismograph is an instrument that automatically registers the various kinds of earthquake waves and the time of their arrival at the seismograph station, producing a graphic record called a seismogram. Seismograph stations have been set up throughout the world, making it possible to determine the depth of an earthquake's focus and the location of its epicenter.

An earthquake's epicenter is located, first, by determining its distance from a recording station. Since P waves travel faster than S waves, the distance between station and epicenter can be measured by the time lapse in the arrival of the different waves.

Once it has been established that an earthquake has occurred, say, 1800 miles from a Chicago station, a circle is drawn using the Chicago station as the center and the 1800 miles (known as the epicentral distance) as the radius. We now know that the epicenter is somewhere on the circle's circumference. If two more circles are drawn from two other stations, the three circles will intersect at a single point. This point will be the epicenter of the earthquake.

Intensity and Magnitude of Earthquakes   The intensity of an earthquake is measured qualitatively, in terms of its destruction of life and property. An earthquake's magnitude is measured on a standard instrument and expresses the total energy released by the earthquake at its source.

The intensities of earthquakes vary from scarcely perceptible to widely destructive. During the largest shocks the energy released is roughly equivalent to 10,000 World War II atom bombs.

A widely known standard for evaluating earthquake intensity is the modified Mercalli scale. On a scale of 12 values, number 1 is "not felt, except by a very few," number 4 is "moderate, felt indoors by many, outdoors by a few," number 7 is "strong, everybody runs outdoors, damage ranges from negligible to considerable" and number 12 is "damage total."

In depicting earthquake intensity, contour lines (called isoseismal lines) are drawn on a map to connect points which have been similarly affected. The area of greatest destruction is in the center, surrounded by areas of diminishing damage.

An earthquake's intensity, of course, will vary from place to place. Its magnitude, however, is always the same. Magnitude is measured by instruments and evaluated on a magnitude scale known as the Richter scale. Each unit indicates an energy release of about 60 times that of the preceding unit. A magnitude of 2 is a barely perceptible shock. A magnitude of 7 is the lower limit of a major destructive earthquake. The highest magnitudes known, both 8.9, were registered in the 1906 Colombia-Ecuador quake and in a Sanriku, Japan, shock in 1933.

Famous Earthquakes　　Earthquakes have disrupted human affairs ever since man appeared on earth. Below are brief descriptions of some of the outstanding quakes of recent history.

Lisbon, 1755. At 9:40 A.M., 10 A.M. and 12 noon on November 1, 1755, All Saints' Day, violent tremors jolted the ancient city of Lisbon, Portugal. The earthquake, one of the most devastating in modern history, was accompanied by rock slides, fires and a huge seismic sea wave which swept up the Tagus River, smashing ships and drowning those who had fled to the pier to escape the burning city. Most of Lisbon's buildings were wrecked by the heaving ground, and more than 60,000 people out of a population of 235,000 perished.

The Lisbon quake may have been the most widely felt in history—its effects were noted in Finland, Scandinavia, England, Germany, Switzerland and northern Italy. Thousands died among the wrecked buildings of Fez and Mequinez, Morocco, 400 miles from Lisbon, and buildings collapsed in dozens of Spanish and North African towns.

New Madrid, 1811–1812. Earthquake tremors rocked the lower Mississippi Valley over a period of 15 months, the first great shock occurring near New Madrid, Missouri, on December 16, 1811, at about two in the morning. During these months the loose soil of the Mississippi bottomlands cracked open, trees fell, log cabins tumbled, river banks caved in, lands rose to drain former swamps or sunk and were flooded by the river to form new lakes.

The quake was America's severest, felt over an area of about one million square miles between Canada and the Gulf of Mexico, the Rockies and the Atlantic. In Boston it stopped clocks and set church bells ringing; in Virginia it cracked plaster. Few lives were endangered, however, because the Mississippi area was very sparsely populated in the pioneering days of 150 years ago.

San Francisco, 1906. In California, from San Bernardino northward, the San Andreas Fault—one of the earth's outstanding fractures—cuts obliquely across the California Coast Ranges for about 600 miles. Over the years movement at various places along the San Andreas Fault has occurred at irregular intervals, resulting in a displacement of at least 15 miles since the Pleistocene Era.

Early on the morning of April 18, 1906, the rocks moved again, the western side of the fault slipping northward while the eastern side slipped southward. About 270 miles of the fault were in motion, and some 375,000 square miles in the San Francisco area were affected by the quake.

Along the fault itself there was a horizontal displacement of as much as 21 feet (near Tomales Bay). Roads, fences, buildings, lines of trees, water pipes—anything that crossed the fault—were sliced and offset. In downtown San Francisco, pavements shattered, buildings collapsed and people were crushed by the debris. More than 700 persons, it is estimated, lost their lives, while property damages exceeded $400 million. Most of this damage, however, was the result of fires—hundreds of them—which raged for days. Started by short circuits, overturned stoves and ruptured gas lines, the fires swept inland from the waterfront while firemen stood by helplessly because the city's water mains were disrupted by the shock.

Yokohama and Tokyo, 1923. On September 1, 1923, shortly before noon, the cities of Tokyo and Yokohama were ravished by an earthquake and the fires it unleashed. The shock, which originated in Sagami Bay, involved a horizontal shift of the entire Tokyo-Yokohama area toward the southeast, with displacements up to 15 feet. There were also vertical displacements up to 6 feet. The quake and fire brought death to some 150,000 people and injured another 100,000. More than 500,000 buildings were destroyed.

Other Major Quakes. The worst earthquake in history occurred in north central China in 1556, when more than 800,000 people lost their lives.

The earthquake of Kutch, near the mouth of the Indus River, caused extensive flooding of the land in 1819, while to the north a 50-mile-long scarp rose as much as 20 feet to form the "Dam of Allah."

In 1855 (and again in 1931) earthquakes in New Zealand tilted and uplifted the land as much as 10 feet.

In 1897 the "Great Assam Earthquake" raised a scarp 35¹ feet and destroyed buildings in Calcutta, 200 miles away.

In 1899 an earthquake in southeastern Alaska produced the greatest vertical displacement known, lifting some areas more than 47 feet above the sea. The shock caused glaciers to recede or move forward, gigantic icebergs to shed—and unleashed tremendous snowslides.

An earthquake in 1908 destroyed the Italian cities of Messina and Reggio, submerging the Messina coast more than 2 feet below its former level and killing about 100,000 people.

Two great earthquakes in western China, one in 1920 and the other in 1927, killed 100,000 people apiece.

In 1950 another earthquake devastated Assam, causing disastrous landslides and floods. The massive landslides had people talking fearfully of a "mountain that walked."

In 1960 three major earthquakes occurred. At Agadir, Morocco, 10,000 people lost their lives. At Lar, Iran, hundreds of buildings collapsed. And along the coast of Chile there was a series of shocks that lasted for more than a month, setting the whole earth vibrating like a gigantic bell.

From the above descriptions it is clear that earthquakes, like volcanoes, have been responsible for terrible losses of life and property. But, like volcanoes, these devastating natural events have provided a precious opportunity to learn about the inaccessible interior of our earth.

Chapter 13 / The Making of Mountains

When a tract of land is distinctively elevated above its surroundings, we call it a mountain. Mountains are made by vulcanism, which builds tall heaps of lava and pyroclastic debris, or forms dome-like blisters (produced by rising bodies of magma). Mountains are also made by diastrophism, which causes the folding and faulting of rocks and the uplifting of great segments of the earth.

Some geologists distinguish between mountains and plateaus—uplifted landmasses whose underlying rocks are nearly flat. Thus the Colorado Plateau, despite its deep stream canyons, is not technically considered a mountain, while many lesser elevations qualify for the honor.

Mountains may be broadly classified as volcanic, fault-block or fold, though there are many that do not fit neatly into any of these categories. Whatever their origin, they are immediately modified by the agents of erosion, which shape, sharpen and cut out the dizzying spires and looming valleys that make mountains a place of special beauty.

VOLCANIC MOUNTAINS

Lava and pyroclastic debris ejected by volcanoes accumulate to form volcanic mountains or mountain chains. Among these are active volcanoes like Fujiyama, linear belts of extinct volcanoes like the Cascades of Oregon and Washington, and submarine volcanoes, like the island arcs of the Pacific.

Volcanic mountains may be small cinder cones or mammoth masses like Mauna Loa, which measures about 30,000 feet from its 90-mile-diameter base on the floor of the sea. Some volcanoes take a solitary, cone-like shape while others are grouped in clusters or chains.

Vulcanism is also responsible for laccolith mountains. These are dome-like formations, raised above the surrounding landscape when rising magma lifts the overlying rock and arches the surface. The Henry Mountains of Utah are an example.

FAULT-BLOCK MOUNTAINS

Fault-block mountains are huge blocks of rock bordered by faults, along which major vertical movements have occurred. No horizontal movement, no folding, no shortening of the earth's crust is required to produce them.

Sometimes vertical movements thrust blocks of rock to mountain height. Sometimes they lower blocks, so that those remaining stand tall relative to their surroundings. Sometimes vertical movements cause blocks to tilt so that one edge rises and the other sinks.

Examples of fault-block mountains can be found in Libya, Mongolia, southern Algeria and the Great Basin region of Utah, Nevada and California. This last region features a series of isolated mountain ranges separated by desert plains, broad basins or rift valleys. Each mountain is formed from a vertically lifted or tilted block of earth's crust and is bounded on at least one side by a steep fault plane. The Sierra Nevada is probably the largest fault-block mountain range on earth. Famous Death Valley is the longest and deepest rift valley in the Great Basin.

FOLD MOUNTAINS

Fold mountains, which appear as a series of alternating ridges and valleys, are linear belts of greatly distorted rock. They are the most numerous of the world's mountains and comprise the greatest ranges. The Alps and the Himalayas are fold mountains, and so are the Appalachians, the Rockies and the Andes.

In all these ranges, the belts of stratified rock are dramatically thicker than rocks of comparable age found in the rest of the continent. Fold mountains are also characterized by deep sialic roots—those of the Alps, for instance, extend downward at least 40 miles.

Fold mountains are the result of a mountain-building process termed orogeny. Orogeny requires an elongated, sediment-receiving trough, called a geosyncline, and horizontal compression of sedimentary rocks.

The shallow trough, filled from time to time with sea water, may be thousands of miles long and hundreds of miles wide. It lies beside a highland and receives the sediments which erode from it. In accordance with isostatic adjustment, the highland rises as it erodes while the trough subsides as the sediments accumulate in the shallow water.

The geosyncline eventually becomes filled with unusually thick sedimentary rock. But although deposits may be as thick as 40,000 feet, the fossils found in them are nearly always those of shallow-water organisms. Geologists consider this strong evidence that a geosyncline is never very deep but instead sinks slowly while sediments continue to be added to it.

Finally the sedimentary layers are depressed to where the rock is more readily susceptible to horizontal compression. Intense folding, faulting, crustal shortening and, perhaps, formation of magma occur, followed by vertical uplift. (Note: Uplift and folding may occur again and again during geosynclinal deposition.)

As soon as the mountains appear, erosion begins. But uplift continues for a while, outpacing the work of water, wind and ice, and so mountains grow taller until a point of isostatic adjustment is reached. Then erosion dominates, gradually reducing mighty ranges to peneplains. (Note: After erosion has wiped out a mountain's relief features and worn it low, uplift may give the mountain a new lease on life.)

There are several examples of geosynclines in the process of receiving sediment today—Italy's Po Valley and India's Valley of the Ganges, for instance. All major mountain ranges now in existence have arisen from past geosynclines squeezed by horizontal movements of the earth.

The Appalachians   These mountains began 500 million years ago as a shallow trough, periodically invaded by an

SEDIMENTARY ROCKS WASHED DOWN FROM HILLS

GEOSYNCLINE 1

In the first stage of orogeny, sediments eroded from a high-land are deposited in a trough called a geosyncline, which sinks slowly as sediments continue to be added.

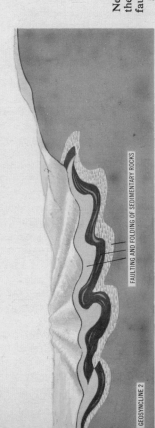

FAULTING AND FOLDING OF SEDIMENTARY ROCKS

GEOSYNCLINE 2

Next, the sedimentary layers in the geosyncline are folded and faulted, vertical uplift occurs, and mountains are formed.

As soon as the mountains appear, erosion begins, gradually reducing mighty ranges to peneplains.

EROSION OF MOUNTAIN TOPS FORMS ALMOST LEVEL PENEPLAIN

GEOSYNCLINE 3

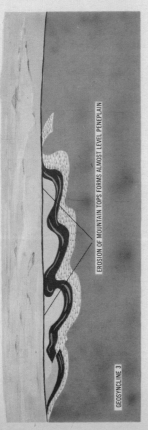

After erosion has worn a mountain low, uplift may raise it again.

UPLIFT RAISES MOUNTAIN

GEOSYNCLINE 4

inland sea, which extended from Newfoundland to Alabama. An eroding highland to the east of the Appalachian geosyncline filled it with sediments until 30,000–40,000 feet were deposited. As the sedimentary materials accumulated, the floor of the trough warped downward.

This period of deposition ended at the close of the Paleozoic Era (for this and other references to the geologic timetable, see the chart at the back of the book). Horizontal compression threw the accumulated sediments into folds or broke them into thrust faults. In places strata were shortened by 25%–30%, or even more.

As soon as the mountains arose, erosion began gnawing at them. Before the Mesozoic Era had ended, the entire region was reduced to a peneplain peppered with monadnocks a few hundred feet high.

In the ensuing periods, vertical movements uplifted the former geosyncline, rejuvenating streams and permitting the sculpting of a second generation of Appalachians.

The Alps   Unlike the ancient Appalachians, the Alps are young and rugged mountains. The accumulation of deposits in the alpine geosyncline did not occur until the Mesozoic and early Cenozoic. Folding and overthrusting did not occur until the Oligocene and early Miocene, a mere 15–40 million years ago.

Horizontal compression of the alpine geosyncline was much greater than compression of the Appalachians. It is interesting to note that northern Italy is today 100 miles closer to northern Switzerland than it was in Eocene time.

The Rockies   This long system of mountains extends from Alaska, where it is called the Brooks Range, down to New Mexico, where it is known as the Southern Rockies. It originated as a geosyncline which received deposits throughout the Paleozoic and Mesozoic. Horizontal compression followed and was completed about 50 million years ago.

UPWARPED MOUNTAINS

These mountains—the Adirondacks and the Black Hills of South Dakota are examples—do not fit comfortably into any of the categories described above. They clearly are not volcanic mountains. And although they may be folded or bordered with faults, they are neither fold nor fault-block mountains. Instead these are dome-like structures formed by the slow upwarping of the rocks, accompanied by erosion.

THEORIES OF MOUNTAIN BUILDING

No one knows the ultimate origin of the internal forces that build mountains. However, a number of hypotheses—some of which will be described below—attempt to explain orogeny in terms of a single underlying cause.

The Contraction Theory This theory begins with a generally accepted assumption—that the earth was once entirely molten. After the crust cooled and solidified, heat loss from the still molten interior caused the interior to contract.

Contraction set up compressional stresses in the crust, which then wrinkled and folded, just as an apple skin does when its core dries and shrinks. Instead of being uniformly distributed, the wrinkles appeared in only a few areas of the earth because the crust had certain zones of weakness. The wrinkles in these zones of weakness are belts of fold mountains.

First postulated more than 100 years ago, this theory is now virtually discredited. Among the many objections raised is the argument that, far from cooling and contracting, the earth's crust may be heating up as a result of radioactivity.

The Continental Drift Theory This theory postulates that all the continents of the earth were once joined together, forming a single protocontinent. Its southern hemisphere has been given the name Gondwanaland.

The protocontinent, says this theory, existed for most of geologic time. Then it broke apart into continental blocks which drifted to their present positions, floating like super-icebergs on top of the quasi-plastic subcrustal material. The friction of the underlying "sea" caused the continents to crumple, forming belts of fold mountains.

Scientists favoring this theory cite the following evi-

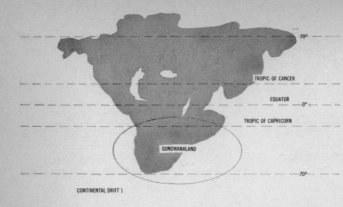

(1) According to the continental drift theory, all the continents once formed a single protocontinent whose southern hemisphere has been named Gondwanaland.

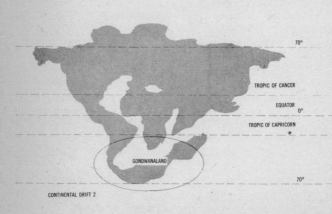

(2) The protocontinent existed for most of geologic time, then broke apart into continental blocks.

70°

TROPIC OF CANCER

EQUATOR 0°

TROPIC OF CAPRICORN

70°

CONTINENTAL DRIFT 3

(3) The blocks, floating like super-icebergs on top of the subcrustal material, drifted to their present positions.

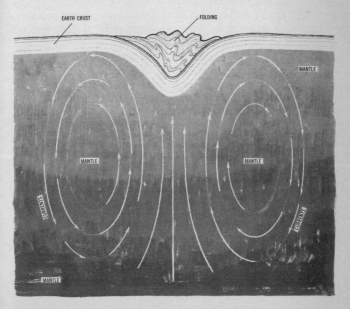

According to the convection current theory, huge oval-shaped "cells" called convection currents exist beneath the earth's crust and are capable of folding solid rock.

dence in its support: (1) the east coast of the Americas fits neatly into the coast of Africa and Europe like pieces of a jigsaw puzzle; (2) the past presence of great ice sheets in what are now the tropics suggests that the continents were once located in very different positions; and (3) fossil-bearing rocks found in South America resemble those found in Africa.

Critics of this theory say that the evidence cited above can be explained in other ways and that continental drift accounts only for recent mountains, not for the older ones. They also object that there is no satisfactory reason given for the breaking up of the protocontinent.

The Convection Current Theory   Many geologists are inclined toward the theory that convection currents beneath the earth's crust move solid rock, just as such currents move the liquid in a pot of boiling water.

According to this theory, sources of great heat in the mantle (centers of intense radioactivity, for instance) generate movement in the form of large currents that rise up from the bottom of the mantle, cross under the crust and then turn downward. It is believed that the mantle, under high pressure and temperature, may behave like a dense liquid, permitting the currents to move slowly in it, perhaps at the rate of an inch or so a year.

The convection currents, this theory continues, take the form of huge oval-shaped "cells" operating in cyclic fashion over many millions of years. For 25 million years, the currents slowly accelerate. For 5–10 million years they operate at peak velocity. For 25 million years the currents decelerate. Then they stop—perhaps for a few hundred million years—until there is sufficient heat to move the rocks of the mantle again. (Note: Different cells would be in different phases of the cycle at any given time.)

Experimental earth models indicate that convection currents could indeed cause folding, overthrusting, crustal shortening and the dragging down of geosynclines. The theory explains uplift, for when the current stops moving, the mountain root is no longer held down and will rise isostatically. Convection currents might also account for the production of magma and the rise of magma to form volcanic extrusions or batholithic intrusions.

Although this is regarded by many as an attractive theory, the actual existence of convection currents beneath the earth's crust has not been established. Thus the origin of the giant forces that buckle and lift the crust into mighty mountains still remains one of geology's most intriguing unknowns.

Chapter 14 / Unlocking the Past

The earth was created, declared a seventeenth-century scholar, at precisely 9 A.M. on October 26, 4004 B.C.

But since that wise doctor's day, scientists have pushed earth's birth date farther and farther back into the past. According to the latest evidence, the age of this planet is an estimated four to five billion years.

In the following chapters we shall examine what is known of earth's history during this unimaginably vast expanse of time, with particular attention to the evolution of life. Speculations concerning the origin of the earth and its life forms, as well as the dating methods which have helped unlock earth's past, are discussed in the sections below.

HOW IT BEGAN

The oldest observable rocks are younger than the earth and can offer almost no hints as to its origin. Speculations about earth's beginnings must leave the realm of geology and consider the solar system as a whole.

Three major theories of earth's origin have been developed and discarded during the past two centuries. The nebular hypothesis was formulated, independently, by the German philosopher Immanuel Kant and the French mathematician and astronomer Pierre Simon de Laplace in the eighteenth century. The planetesimal hypothesis was proposed about a hundred years later by American geologist T. C. Chamberlin and astronomer F. R. Moulton. Sir James Jeans, a physicist, and astronomer Sir Harold Jeffreys conceived the tidal hypothesis in the early part of the twentieth century.

The Nebular Hypothesis According to this hypothesis, the solar system began as an intensely hot gaseous mass rotating slowly in space. This nebula, as it was called, was so enormous that it encompassed the orbit of the outermost planet, Pluto.

Gradually the nebula cooled and contracted, and its rotational velocity increased. As it spun faster and faster, centrifugal force built up until fiery gas rings—similar to the rings that surround Saturn—were cast off from the parent nebula. Meanwhile the central body of the nebula contracted to form the sun.

The matter in each of the cast-off gas rings gathered by gravitation into the nine planets of our solar system. They too contracted, sloughing off rings as they spun. These are the planets' moons and other satellites.

The nebular hypothesis requires that the sun, remnant of the rotating gas cloud, spin quite rapidly in space. Since it has been established that the sun actually rotates rather slowly, this theory has been rejected.

The Planetesimal Hypothesis Kant and Laplace viewed the earth as cooling from gas to liquid to solid. The planetesimal hypothesis proposed that the earth was solid from the start, growing by accretion around a central core.

The sun, according to this theory, existed as a star before the planets were formed. The close approach of another, passing star exerted strong gravitational pull on the sun, raising tides upon it and eventually tearing away great "bolts" of gaseous material.

This material cooled to a liquid and then to a vast cloud of dust whose individual particles were named planetesimals. These orbited around the sun, colliding with each other again and again. Larger clusters of planetesimals served as nuclei around which others accumulated, eventually forming the earth and other planets. Smaller planetesimals, located near the planets, became their satellites.

The Tidal Hypothesis This theory also begins with a close encounter between the sun and a passing star. Tides were raised and a long single filament of glowing gas was pulled away. In this modification of the planetesimal hypothesis, however, the material torn from the sun remained a gas as it broke up into planets rotating in space. Thus the earth, according to Jeans and Jeffreys, was originally a gas, later cooling to a liquid and then to a solid state.

Neither the planetesimal nor the tidal hypothesis explains all the features of the solar system. They have been generally rejected in favor of a return to some type of nebular hypothesis of earth origin, like the one below.

The Protoplanet Hypothesis   The solar system began, says this theory, as an enormous nebula of gas and dust moving very slowly in space. Later it condensed and speeded up. The outer part of the nebula flattened into a thin disc in which turbulent eddies of gas and dust particles swirled. The friction of these different particles slowed the rotation of the central mass (which later became the sun) and made the outer parts (which later became the planets) move faster. This is why the sun rotates far more slowly than most of the planets, a fact that the somewhat similar nebular hypothesis was unable to account for.

When the outer part of the nebula broke from the sun, it first formed protoplanets, orbiting bodies which were much larger than the earth and the other planets of our solar system today. But they too cooled, contracted and moved faster, and satellites formed from them just as the planets themselves had formed from the original nebula.

Variations of this theory propose that the protoplanets were solid instead of gaseous, and were much smaller than today's planets. The present size of the earth, these current variations suggest, is the result of the accretion of solid particles.

THE NEW EARTH

The geological history of earth can be traced from its oldest known rocks. But no record exists for the interval of pre-geological (as in prehistoric) time that lies between the formation of the earth and the formation of its continents and ocean basins.

It was during this pregeological time that the earth cooled and the rocks of the crust began to solidify. At first the crust was weak and thin and easily broken, with great upwellings of lava from below. But eventually the lighter granitic rocks gathered to form the continental platforms while the heavier basalt formed the ocean basins.

The origin of the continents and ocean basins has, like the origin of the earth itself, been a subject of much hypothesizing.

According to one hypothesis, the crust of the earth was originally homogeneous. It simply cooled and separated into granite and basalt, the heavier basalt solidifying first and sinking to form the ocean basins, while the lighter granite eventually formed the continents.

But perhaps, says another theory, the crust was not homogeneous. Instead, granite might have dominated in some areas and basalt in others. Such a distribution would explain the location as well as the formation of the continents.

The theory of continental drift, discussed in the preceding chapter, also presumes that the original crust had local concentrations of granite and basalt. It suggests, however, that in the beginning there was only one protocontinent, which later broke into smaller parts. These drifted through the heavier basaltic underlayer until they reached their present positions.

Another hypothesis postulates that there were no continents at all early in earth's history. Instead, the solidified crust was essentially basalt, with gases and lava escaping to the surface through cracks. Water vapor condensed to water, while the other gases formed the atmosphere. Meanwhile the lava built volcanic chains like those seen in today's island arcs. These later became granitic, and served as the base on which the continents built up by accretion. According to this theory, the continents are growing bigger and bigger.

Still another hypothesis proposes that when the earth cooled, a granitic layer lay over the entire surface. The planet expanded, cracking the granitic crust and breaking it into segments separated by basalt. The ocean basins have enlarged to their present size from these original cracks in the earth. According to this theory, the continents have remained the same size but the earth is getting larger.

While the continents and ocean basins were being formed (in any of the ways postulated above), water vapor and other gases probably rose from the interior and settled over the earth in massive cloudbanks. Perhaps, from time to time, these clouds condensed into rain, but the heat of earth's crust instantly boiled away the falling waters. Eventually, however, the crust cooled below the boiling point and a monumental flood filled the ocean basins with about 20% of the water they hold today. The rest of the water was squeezed up through the basaltic basins from the earth's interior.

Once the ocean basins and dry land areas were established, the processes of erosion, transportation and deposition began. The sedimentary history of the earth started to accumulate. The period of pregeological time was at an end.

THE EVOLUTION OF LIFE

Life appeared on earth perhaps three billion years ago, during the span of geologic time termed Precambrian. According to one view, all species of plants and animals were separately created at about the same time by a divine being. According to another view, the seeds of life were carried here on meteorites. But modern scientists tend toward the theory that life on earth developed from non-life, originating in the water rather than on land.

Perhaps, it is suggested, solar radiation and other forces acted upon elements present in our early atmosphere to produce organic compounds, particularly amino acids, which are part of all living organisms. Perhaps these small molecules united and grew more complex, finally forming the first organism capable of reproducing itself.

Beginning, probably, as a one-celled microscopic organism, life has evolved through the ages from simple to increasingly complex and generally more intelligent forms. It is intriguing to discover that the life history of man (ontogeny), as he grows from single cell to adult, recapitulates in a general way the historical development of the race (phylogeny).

The theory of evolution was compellingly formulated by Charles Darwin in his historic work *On the Origin of Species by Means of Natural Selection,* published on November 24, 1859. Darwin asserted that all organisms exhibit variability and that they produce many more off-spring than the environment can support. He concluded that the environment selects those best fitted for survival; that these organisms mature, reproduce and pass on their favorable characteristics to the next generation; and that the unfit perish. Eventually the characteristics of a species change and new species arise.

Prior to Darwin, in 1801, the paleontologist Jean Baptiste Lamarck proposed that the inheritance of acquired characteristics accounted for evolutionary change. He said giraffes, for instance, began with a short-necked ancestor which had to stretch its neck to reach high leaves on the tree. The stretched neck was passed on through succeeding generations, becoming progressively longer as the giraffe stretched—and stretched—and stretched.

Darwin's natural selection concept, on the other hand, began with an ancestral giraffe group in which there were necks of varying lengths. The long-necks, better able to reach the high leaves than the short-necks, got most of the food and were therefore best able to survive. They lived to mate with other long-necks, producing offspring possessing this useful characteristic. As one generation yielded to the next, giraffes developed increasingly long necks.

The theory of evolution is supported by observation and experimentation, by embryology and paleontology and by comparative physiology and comparative anatomy. The most convincing evidence is the record of the fossils—remains of the plants and animals of the past—which show the development of life from ancient times to the present.

FOSSILS

Fossils are many things. They may be the original hard parts of organisms, some as old as 100 million years. A bone or a seashell of the distant past is a fossil. So are logs of wood from prehistoric forests.

The soft parts of organisms tend to decay swiftly after death. Fascinating exceptions are the complete (flesh and all) bodies of Ice Age mammoths and rhinoceroses, preserved in the frozen tundra of the North. These are fossils too.

Fossils are also the petrified (turned-to-stone) hard parts of organisms. Petrifaction (also called petrification) may occur when ground water invades the pores of bones and shells, laying down mineral matter. This process, called permineralization, has petrified the bones of huge dinosaurs.

Petrifaction may involve, in some cases, the substitution of the mineral matter from ground water for the original organic substance. This process, called replacement, is responsible for the fossils known as petrified wood.

Sometimes petrifaction involves the loss of an organism's volatile elements and the concentration of its carbon content, the residue forming a perfect outline of the original. This process, called carbonation, has left us with beautifully etched fossil fern leaves.

Tracks, footprints and burrows are fossils. Classic examples are the thousands of dinosaur footprints seen in

A natural cast of fossil shells.

the shaly sandstone of the Connecticut River Valley. The burrows of worms are among the oldest of all fossils.

A natural mold is formed in a rock where an organism was once embedded but later disappeared, leaving an empty space having the object's exact form. Molds of insects are found in Baltic amber. A natural cast, produced when a natural mold was subsequently filled with mineral matter, is also a fossil.

Still other fossils are coprolites, the excrement of ancient animal life, which reveals animal feeding habits.

Fossils may be preserved in marine and fresh-water sediments, in arctic tundra, in lava and volcanic ash and in other burial places. Although there are many forms of life which are, strictly speaking, neither plant nor animal, these two kingdoms serve as the major classifications under which most fossils are grouped.

Fossils not only furnish the data from which we can

retrace the changing history of life on earth. They indicate
the presence, thousands or millions of years ago, of seas
where there is now dry land, of land connections where
now there is only sea. They provide clues to the nature
of climates that existed in days long before there were
weathermen—or any men at all—to record them. And,
as will be seen below, fossils also make it possible to determine the succession within a rock series and to correlate
rock formations in far distant corners of the world, thus
helping to date the earth.

DATING THE EARTH

The position of rock layers, the fossils they contain and
the disintegration of their radioactive elements have enabled geologists to date the earth in both relative and
absolute terms. Relative age indicates sequence—whether
something is younger or older than something else. Absolute age is a measure of how old—in actual years—that
something is.

Relative Age   Long before it was possible to assign specific dates to rocks, geologists had discovered certain principles which enabled them to determine a rock layer's relative
age.

1.   In a series of sedimentary rock layers, younger
rocks normally lie on top of older rocks.

2.   Igneous rocks are younger than the rocks they
intrude.

3.   Unless disturbed, the strata in a given area always
occur in the same order.

4.   Different rock layers contain their own distinctive
assemblages of fossils.

5.   Like assemblages of fossil organisms (called
faunal assemblages) indicate like geologic ages for the
rocks that contain them.

6.   Once a species dies out, it never reappears in
younger strata.

Applying these principles, geologists have established
the standard geologic column, which indicates the sequence

of rock deposits from oldest to youngest and the fossils characteristic of each bed.

There are many gaps in the standard column, for a complete record of the rocks exists nowhere on earth. These gaps are known as unconformities, and indicate periods of non-deposition or periods when layers were removed by erosion before later ones were added.

Having established an order of deposition, however, geologists can now compare a succession of rocks in one locale with entirely different ones elsewhere, using fossil assemblages to correlate and help close the gaps. The most reliable criteria are the so-called index fossils—those which have been distributed over a wide area, have had a relatively short existence and have changed rapidly during their time on earth.

Absolute Age In 1654 James Ussher, Archbishop of Armagh (Ireland), calculated the absolute age of the earth, basing his arithmetic on studies of the Scriptures. His conclusion—that the Creation had taken place in 4004 B.C. —became so fixed in religious thinking that for years it was considered heretical to deny it.

In the nineteenth century, however, it became clear that the forces which shaped the earth required a far longer stretch of time to have done their work. There followed several ingenious efforts to establish earth's absolute age on a more scientific basis.

Some geologists believed that the age of rocks could be determined by estimating the total thickness of the sedimentary rock layers laid down since the beginning of geologic time and dividing this figure by the present annual rate of deposition. In 1899 the British geologist Sollas, using this method, concluded that the length of time since the start of the Palezoic (see Geologic Time Chart, back of book) could have been anywhere from 34 to 75 million years. He was off, according to modern dating, by at least 525 million years.

There were several things wrong with this approach. The most important flaw is that there is no such figure as "an average rate of deposition." Rates of deposition differ, depending on the kind of rock and on the circumstances under which deposition occurs. It may take a century to deposit less than an inch of chalk, while 40 feet of gravel may be laid down in an hour during a desert cloudburst. A Mississippi flood can deposit 5 feet of mud in 24 hours, while it might require thousands of years for only 1 foot of mud to accumulate at the bottom of a lake.

Another turn-of-the-century scientist, John Joly, attempted to determine the age of the sea by comparing its present salt content to the amount of salt added annually. Estimates of both figures were obtainable, but the result of his arithmetic—99.4 million years—was completely off-base.

Where did Joly go wrong? First, he assumed that the amount of salt eroded from rocks and transported by rivers to the sea has been constant throughout geologic time. This is unlikely. Second, he ignored the vast deposits of rock salt which came from evaporated sea water. He also left several other factors out of his calculations, like the amount of salt carried off from the sea by blowing winds.

A reasonably reliable method used today to determine the absolute age of rocks (and of the earth) is radioactive dating. Radioactive dating techniques have placed the age of the earth's oldest known rocks—those in central Canada, western Australia, the Ukraine and the Kola Peninsula of the Soviet Union—as between $2\frac{1}{2}$ and $3\frac{1}{2}$ billion years. The age of the earth itself—based on the dating of meteorites—is estimated to be 4–5 billion years.

Radioactivity is the spontaneous disintegration of certain radioactive elements into other elements at a constant rate of decay, expressed as an element's "half-life." A half-life is the time required for half a given amount of material to disintegrate into a final product.

Decay rates vary enormously from element to element. The half-life of uranium 238 is 4.507 billion years, while the half-life of carbon 14 is only about 5568 years.

One gram of U^{238}, then, decays to $\frac{1}{2}$ gram in 4.507 billion years, $\frac{1}{4}$ gram in another 4.507 billion years. The other half (or three-fourths) changes eventually to lead. Once a scientist is able to determine the exact amount of uranium in a host rock and the exact amount of lead formed from the decay of uranium, the age of the rock can be determined too.

Carbon 14, with its very short half-life, is of no use in dating ancient rocks. But the age of materials under 40,000 years old can be established with this convenient radioactive clock.

Other radioactive elements—like thorium and rubidium—are also used to establish the age of rocks.

All radioactive dating methods entail very precise chemical analyses and there is plenty of room for error. Nevertheless, it is an extremely useful method—the best available at this time.

The Geologic Time Scale Thanks to radioactive dating, we can now not only verify the sequence of rock units in the standard geologic column but also assign specific ages to them. The result is the geologic time scale (see back of book), divided into major segments called eras and further subdivided into periods and epochs.

Virtually everything we know about the history of life on earth took place in the Paleozoic Era (when invertebrates and simple vertebrates dominated), the Mesozoic (when reptiles dominated) and the Cenozoic (when mammals dominated). But some 80%–85% of earth's history occurred before the Paleozoic, in a period of about four billion years known as Precambrian time.

PRECAMBRIAN TIME

The first period of the Paleozoic Era is called the Cambrian. Beginning 600 million years ago, it marked the first appearance of abundant fossil records. But below the Cambrian strata lie thousands of feet of sediment, with only faint traces of plant and animal remains. These were formed during Precambrian time, the vast geologic span lying between the beginning of earth history and the start of the Cambrian.

Throughout most of the continents, Precambrian rocks are buried under younger ones. They are exposed, however, in the large, relatively low-relief-shield areas of the earth, in the cores of folded mountain ranges and in the bottoms of deep canyons, like the Inner Gorge of the Grand Canyon.

The largest surface area of Precambrian rock covers about half of Canada and is known as the Canadian or Laurentian shield. There are also extensive outcrops in South America (the Guianan and Amazonian shields), Europe (the Baltic shield of Scandinavia and Finland), India (the Indian shield), Siberia (the Angara shield), Africa (the Ethiopian shield) and Australia (the Australian shield). The shield areas were very active tectonically during the Precambrian, but since the start of the Paleozoic Era they have been relatively stable.

Very little is known of earth's climate during Precambrian time, but there is nothing to indicate that it was much different from the climates of later eras. The rocks bear witness, however, to the occurrence of extreme glaciation during the Precambrian—in North America, Australia, South Africa and China, in India, Greenland and Norway.

Only the faintest fossil records—the traces of burrows, the trails of worm-like animals, the remains of simple lime-secreting algae and mysterious organic structures as yet unidentified—are imprinted in the ancient Precambrian rocks. Nevertheless, these are sufficient to indicate the presence—small, undistinguished, but indisputably there—of life on earth.

UNLOCKING THE PAST

The geologic timetable tells us that the earth is about 4½ billion years old, that the first abundant fossil records appeared 600 million years ago, that man first appeared about a million years ago, and that modern man has evolved in the past 50,000 years.

It has been suggested that we visualize this entire expanse of time as a single year. Looking at earth history from this perspective, the fossil record is 40 days old, man arrived 2 hours ago and modern man has been on the scene for only 5 minutes.

A high-speed camera, attempting to record the events of this year, would show a repeated rise and fall of the land, a repeated inundation and withdrawal of the sea. For time and again, vulcanism and diastrophism have built enormous mountains. And time and again, water, wind and ice have brought them low. As the land was washed into the sea, the sea level was slowly raised and the waters invaded the worn-down continent. As the sea level dropped and the crust was elevated, the ocean withdrew from the land. Mild or tropical climates alternated with cold, even glacial climates. Living things adapted to these changes, or perished forever from the earth.

Until the beginning of the Paleozoic Era, these events of earth's history were unclear. With the appearance of abundant fossils, however, it became far easier to read the story of the rocks.

"The difference between Precambrian and the Paleozoic," writes geologist Richard M. Pearl, "is like that between a well-printed book in our own language and a fragmentary manuscript written in a strange tongue."

Chapter 15 / The Paleozoic Era

The Paleozoic Era—the Era of Ancient Life—began 600 million years ago and lasted, altogether, about 400 million years. It was punctuated by seven periods of unequal duration—the Cambrian (600–500 million years ago), the Ordovician (500–440 million), the Silurian (440–400 million), the Devonian (400–350 million), the Mississippian and Pennsylvanian, also called the Carboniferous (350–270 million) and the Permian (270–225 million).

During this era, monumental changes occurred on the planet. Earth movements built the Appalachians and other new mountains, reshaping the outlines of the continents and altering the climate. Animals and plants finally left the warm waters of their birth, bringing action, color and sound to the barren rocks of the land. Forests of skyscraping trees grew from humble marine algae, and from primitive invertebrates emerged the first creatures to possess that great symbol of the higher beasts—a backbone.

GEOGRAPHY AND CLIMATE

In each period of the Paleozoic, the seas rolled shallowly over the interior of the continents. Most periods ended with uplifts that raised the continents above water level, draining the oceans back to their basins again. Frequently the emergence of the continents coincided with the building of mountains in some part of the world.

North America, at the start of the Paleozoic, is pictured as a broad, stable, low-lying interior region framed by slowly subsiding geosynclines, each of which was supplied, for much of the era, with sediments eroded from fringing islands which have subsequently vanished.

In the East, its position approximating that of the present Appalachians, lay the Appalachian geosyncline (and a temporarily separated branch called the Acadian trough).

In the West, lying between the present Rockies and the Pacific Coast Ranges, the Cordilleran geosyncline sprawled from the Pacific Ocean in southern California to the Arctic Ocean in the North.

In the South, the Ouachita geosyncline extended across Oklahoma, Texas and northern Mexico.

In the Northeast lay the ancient Canadian shield of Precambrian time.

The Cambrian was characterized by a mild climate and—in the late Cambrian—high waters, conditions which continued without widespread land emergence in the United States into the next period. The greatest flooding ever to occur in North America took place in Ordovician time. At least half of the continent was submerged under the warm epicontinental waters and every part of the Canadian shield was covered. The period culminated in the first of the Paleozoic's major mountain-building episodes, the Taconic orogeny, which produced the Taconic Mountains of eastern New York. By the close of the Ordovician, the waters had withdrawn from most of the continent.

In the Silurian period the seas again encroached and again withdrew. The waters were warm and the climate mild, but later it became increasingly arid. No pronounced orogenic movements occurred in North America between Silurian and Devonian times, but great folding and faulting (the Caledonian orogeny) took place in the northern part of the British Isles.

The Devonian period began with Appalachia worn low, but it was later raised by the Acadian orogeny, which produced the Acadian Range running from Newfoundland perhaps as far south as North Carolina. The central lowlands were warped into arches and domes, structures which can still be seen today in many places. Most of the West lay under the sea. Evidence of a land connection between North America and Europe, believed to have existed in the early and middle Paleozoic, can be found in Devonian rocks. In some areas the climate grew more and more arid, interrupted by heavy seasonal rains. Great belts of sandy desert appeared in many parts of the world.

Widespread earth movements began in the Mississippian period, continued through the Pennsylvanian and, in the case of the Appalachian and Ouachitan geosynclines, reached their grand climax in the Permian. These movements not only made mountains, but also raised former sea beds into flat swamps, perhaps like the Everglades. The vast swampy plains and the increasingly warm, moist climate of the Carboniferous supported lush forests, in Europe as well as in North America, from whose decaying vegetation have come today's abundant coal resources.

The Permian period ushered in a series of dramatic changes unexcelled by any previous period of the Paleozoic. The entire Ouachita geosyncline was compressed from the southeast, forming the Ouachita Mountains. The Appalachian Revolution climaxed with the wrinkling, cracking and faulting of rocks from Newfoundland to Alabama, forming the lofty Appalachian Mountains. The waters withdrew from the continents.

The Permian climate contrasted dramatically with the uniform warmth and humidity of the Carboniferous. Instead of a planet-wide Indian summer, there were extremes of bitter cold and broiling heat, heavy rains, great aridity and intense glaciation. Glaciers were particularly notable in the Southern Hemisphere, where ice locked the lands of South America, South Africa and Australia. The mark of Permian glaciers has been found within 20° of the equator in India, and within 10° of the equator in Brazil!

PLANT LIFE

When the Paleozoic began, marine algae—including many species of seaweed—were just about the only plants on earth. These early, primitive forms, known as non-vascular plants, were poorly equipped for life on the land for they had no true leaves, no stems, no roots and no well-developed internal mechanism for conducting food and water.

Still, such non-vascular plants were—in the Silurian —the first living organisms to leave the water, coating seaside rocks and venturing into marshlands and other moist but not entirely submerged habitats. The next step was the emergence—in early Devonian—of primitive vascular plants, almost all of them members of a group called Psilophytales. They too confined themselves to coastal marshes and other well-watered areas.

By mid-Devonian, more-developed forms had forested large areas of the bare landscape with flowerless green growths. They had roots to suck moisture from the soil, rigid skeletons to hold themselves erect, and simple leaves to catch the sunlight. They no longer needed a watery environment in order to survive.

The evolution of Paleozoic plant life reached its peak during the Pennsylvanian period—the time of the great coal forests. Small plants grew to tree size, and spread throughout the world.

Among the most common flora of that time was *Calamites,* a tall reed-like plant that averaged from 15 to 20 feet but sometimes soared as high as 40. These super-sized relatives of the modern horsetail or scouring rush were slim and tapering, with a core of pith, ribbed and jointed woody stems, a circle of branches at each of the joints, a circle of leaves at each of the branches, and cones that sometimes measured a foot long and an inch around. *Calamites* grew in swampy areas, forming dense jungles.

Another common plant of the Carboniferous was *Cordaites,* ancestor of today's coniferous firs and pines. Nearly 100 feet high, the graceful *Cordaites* generally bore branches only at the upper portion of the trunk. These were covered generously with leaves, either narrow and grass-like, or long and slim and strap-shaped, or broad and spatulate.

Tree ferns were also important during the Carboniferous. They often reached heights of 70 feet, with 2-foot-diameter trunks and a topping of large, spreading, compound leaves. Seed ferns, bearing seeds instead of spores, were present too. Perhaps they were the forerunners of all the higher seed-bearing plants.

The giants of the coal forests were the towering "scale trees," or lycopods, represented by *Lepidodendron* and *Sigillaria.*

Lepidodendron, it is estimated, was more than 135

feet tall. It had a narrow, tapered trunk and paired branches near the top. Awl-shaped leaves, set in a close spiral, left diamond-shaped scars arranged in oblique rows around the stem when they fell. The tips of *Lepidodendron* branches bore cones that were sometimes 20 inches long.

Sigillaria, which was generally found where *Lepidodendron* grew, reached heights of 100 or more feet. Its leaves, sword-shaped and about 3 feet in length, massed in a cluster at the top, making hexagonal scars arranged in vertical rows when they fell. Like *Lepidodendron, Sigillaria* put out cones. They grew in clusters around the trunk, just below the leaves.

This rich profusion of plant life flourished in the subtropical environment of the Carboniferous. Layer after layer of decaying matter piled upon the swampy plain, forming peat and, ultimately, coal. All the world's major coal fields originated in the Pennsylvanian period.

Many Pennsylvanian forms—the scale trees and *Calamites,* for instance—persisted into the early Permian. Eventually, however, they were defeated by the cold and aridity of this final period of the Paleozoic.

The best-known and most controversial Permian plant assemblage is the *Glossopteris* flora. *Glossopteris* was a seed fern, the small and hardy relative of the cycads. Its fossil remains appear in the Southern Hemisphere in South America, South Africa, Australia and Antarctica. It has also been found in India.

The presence of *Glossopteris* in these far-flung portions of the world, some scientists say, is evidence that the continent of Gondwanaland once existed. They maintain that physical connections between the separate lands of the Southern Hemisphere are the only way to account for the widespread distribution of these plants.

ANIMAL LIFE

The presence of abundant fossils at the start of the Cambrian is due to the development of hard parts. Soft-bodied organisms, like those living in Precambrian time, are rarely preserved. But the rigid shells and plates that served as protection for the Cambrian sea dwellers have left ample imprints in the rocks.

Cambrian and Ordovician animal life was almost exclusively invertebrate, and included representatives of all the major invertebrate groups (phyla). Generally, however, the early Paleozoic forms of each phylum were simpler and less specialized than those appearing later.

Among the early backboneless organisms moving through the warm ocean waters were the microscopic radiolarians and foraminifers, both members of the phylum Protozoa. They have persisted from the Cambrian period to the present day, their remains forming great layers of solid rock which have later been uplifted as dry land. Both are among the most important index fossils of the Paleozoic.

The radiolarian is an amoeba-like organism with an elaborate external skeleton of silica—delicate and lovely and frequently decorated with long spiny projections. The foraminifer, also amoeba-like, has a calcium carbonate shell that may have several interconnected chambers—straight, curved or spinal-shaped. It lives in all the chambers and can build on annexes merely by secreting a new wall.

Another Cambrian sea dweller still represented in modern times is the sponge—phylum Porifera—significant because it was one of the first instances of single cells assembling into a complex organism with specialized parts. That is, certain cells absorbed food; others protected the organism; still others reproduced, and so on.

Jellyfish (phylum Coelenterata), gastropod mollusks and marine worms were also present 500 million years ago. Lampshells, so called because of their resemblance to old Roman lamps, account for a third of all Cambrian fossils. These small marine animals, members of phylum Brachiopoda, had a double hinged shell usually only 1 or 2 inches across. When the shell opened, two coiled appendages or brachia extended to capture particles of food.

Ruler of the period, however, was not the brachiopod but the trilobite—phylum Arthropoda—one of the highest forms of life in its time. These Cambrian kings, comparable in status to the dinosaurs of later periods, averaged an

The trilobite of the phylum Arthropoda was
one of the highest forms of life in its time.

inch or two in length, and even the rare giants among
them grew no larger than 2 feet. Trilobites probably developed from soft-bodied, segmented worms, progressing
from pinhead-sized, eyeless creatures to grotesque, highly
ornamented forms with complex, multilensed eyes.

The name trilobite derives from the three divisions, or
lobes, that marked the shell of its upper surface. It had
three major body parts—head, thorax and tail. In keeping
with the triplet form its legs, sometimes two dozen pairs
of them, had three functions: part of the leg was used for
swimming, another part was used for walking, and spiny
projections on the leg's inner side, serving as a kind of
external jaw, were used to chew food.

Some trilobites swam freely at the surface of the
water. Others were found near the shore, occupying the
shallow waters. And still others were scavengers and bur-
rowers in the mud at the bottom of the sea.

Trilobites and brachiopods persisted in the Ordovician, while other invertebrates increased in number, size and variety. Three colonial groups—the corals, the graptolites (among the most valuable index fossils of Paleozoic history) and the "moss animals" (phylum Bryozoa) built intricate sea dwellings, the corals really coming into their own in the next period, when they appeared in all the oceans of the world. A marine bristle worm, which secreted a calcareous, tube-shaped dwelling, lived during the Ordovician. Clams and starfish appeared.

The cephalopod, probably the largest of all Ordovician life forms, became master of the sea. This ancient representative of phylum Mollusca, relative of the squid and octopus, was encased in a straight or tightly coiled hard shell up to 15 feet long. (The name cephalopod means "head-foot" and refers to the tentacles surrounding the mouth, giving the appearance of a circlet of limbs.)

Among the fossils embedded in Ordovician rocks have been found the most important remains of all—the first faint traces of vertebrate life, perhaps as old as 450 million years. Vertebrates are the main members of the phylum Chordata, the highest phylum of the animal kingdom.

Chordates include a few other animals, too, all qualifying as creatures with notochords—the embryonic backbone. The notochord is found today in the modern tunicate or sea squirt, in the primitive acorn worm and in the lancelet. It is the forerunner of the typical backbone of the higher animals with its individual bones (vertebrae), its bony projections (spines) and its hollow tube (neural canal) which runs through the vertebrae and contains the main nerve cord. Startling proof of the evolution of backbone from notochord is the fact that every vertebrate embryo—including man—possesses a notochord!

But we are rushing the vertebrate story. The Ordovician remains were merely small flakes of bone. It was not until late Silurian that complete vertebrate skulls and skeletons were available.

During the Silurian period the brachiopods and nautiloids continued to thrive, as did the sponges and clams. There were a number of coral groups, including colonial forms that built great fringing reefs. Although the trilobites were still present, they were clearly on the decline. The predatory eurypterid, a scorpion-like creature that some-

times measured more than 9 feet long, became the dominant figure of the animal kingdom.

Eurypterids had oar-like limbs well-suited for swimming. Unlike trilobites, they were not limited to the
sea. Instead, many of them migrated up the rivers and
into fresh waters. When these waters dried up, most of
their inhabitants died. But some eurypterid relatives ad-
justed, eventually becoming centipedes and millepedes,
scorpions and spiders and flying insects.

Crinoids or sea lilies, flowery-looking members of the
phylum Echinodermata, were so prevalent in the Silurian
seas that this period is often called the Age of Sea Lilies.
These animals had a long, segmented, limy stem which
anchored them to the sea floor. Branching, petal-like tentacles surrounded the mouth, reeling in bits of food as they
fluttered in the water.

By far the most significant event of the Silurian was
the appearance of primitive jawless fish, called ostracoderms, which probably originated in fresh, not ocean,
water. These archaic vertebrates had, instead of a mouth, a
small hole or crosswise slit. Instead of paired limbs or
fins they wore a pair of flaps behind the head, or small
spines at the sides. And instead of an internal bony skeleton
they were equipped with thick plates of bony armor, which
probably served to protect them from the predatory eurypterids.

Ostracoderms, primitive as they were, were preceded
by still more primitive vertebrate forms. And somewhere
even earlier in their history lurks an invertebrate ancestor.
Was it a worm? An arthropod? Scientists have considered
both these and many other possibilities. Currently favored
is the Echinodermata—the phylum that includes the starfish, the sea urchin and the sea lily. It may well be that
from this unlikely group has followed all backboned life,
including man.

Before looking at the animals of the Devonian, it will
be useful to examine some of the reasons for the ascend-
ancy of vertebrate life in all succeeding periods of earth's
history.

To begin with, the vertebrate's strong but flexible
internal skeleton permits greater freedom of movement

than the awkward and heavy external shell of invertebrate creatures. It also permits uninterrupted growth.

The vertebrate skull, roomy and well-protected, allows the development of a more sophisticated brain.

The nerve cord, which controls animal movements, is safely sheathed in the vertebrate backbone.

Paired organs—two eyes, two lungs, two kidneys— give vertebrates a second chance at survival if one of these valuable organs is impaired.

And the grouping of the main sense organs in the front of the head, and the specialization of the limbs and body for locomotion, result in an animal more efficient and more mobile than most invertebrate forms.

All these features help explain why, despite the invertebrates' enormous numerical superiority, vertebrates have dominated life since the Age of Fishes—the name given to the Devonian period.

At the start of the Devonian, starfish and other echinoderms were on the increase; gaily colored sea lilies covered the rocks of the ocean; and the lampshells headed for their evolutionary peak. During this period, too, animals finally made their break from the water. Tiny invertebrate forms —millepedes and wingless insects, small scorpions and spiders—were the earliest pioneers, tempted by the new food supply and the safety land offered from large marine predators. But eventually these first settlers were followed by the vertebrates.

The development of vertebrate life during the Devonian was dramatic. From ostracoderms evolved placoderms, fish with paired fins, jaws and primitive teeth. Like the ostracoderms, the first placoderms were fresh-water dwellers. But later they invaded the sea.

From as yet unknown placoderm ancestors evolved sharks and bony fishes. The latter diverged into two basic groups, the ray-finned fishes—represented today by all the common fishes—and the Choanichthyes (fish with internal nostrils) which had lungs as well as gills. These lungs enabled Choanichthyes to take in oxygen directly from the air.

Among the Choanichthyes was a branch named the crossopterygians, also known as fringe-fins or lobe-fins.

The lobe-finned fish *Eusthenopteron,* a member of the Crossopterygians, not only breathed air but supported their fins with muscular lobes that could be adapted for walking on land.

The *Diplovertebron*, an amphibian, possessed a long, slim body, a well-developed tail, and limbs capable of locomotion on land.

They not only breathed air but supported their fins with muscular lobes that could be adapted for walking on land. (Until recently it was believed that crossopterygians had been extinct for about 70 million years. But in 1939, off East London, South Africa, a fisherman brought up a peculiar-looking 5-foot fish with large bluish scales. This unique creature turned out to be a coelacanth, member of the crossopterygian group, relative of the ancestors of all land vertebrates.)

The first vertebrate land dwellers of the Devonian were some unknown representatives of the crossopterygians. From them evolved amphibians—the most primitive and earliest known of our four-footed animals. These schizophrenic creatures can live on the land but must return to the water to breed.

In the case of most amphibians, eggs are laid and fertilized in the water and the young are born there. Many pass through a fish-like stage (like tadpoles) before developing legs and learning to breathe with lungs (like frogs). Only then can the amphibian leave its aquatic home to dwell in the damp environs of the shore.

Living amphibians include frogs and toads, salamanders and newts, and some rare worm-like forms. But all have descended from older and far more primitive forms, among them the labyrinthodonts, well represented in Carboniferous deposits.

Diplovertebron was one of the most successful of these ancient labyrinthodonts. Its long slim body, well-developed tail and many of its internal features closely resemble those of the lobe-finned crossopterygians. But the critical difference between this amphibian and its fishy ancestors was the presence of limbs capable of locomotion on land.

Later amphibian forms made increasingly successful adaptations to life on the land. The well-known genus *Eryops,* of Permian time, spent most of its life outside the water. A stocky, thick-set creature, *Eryops* measured about 5 feet in length and had short, powerful, sprawling limbs. It probably lived somewhat the way an alligator does, prowling along the banks of pools and streams, slipping into the water and out again.

Scientists do not believe that amphibians developed

limbs in order to leave the water. Instead, they point out that water dwellers, helpless when their pools shrank and dried during the Devonian's arid spells, developed legs in order to travel overland to reach another pool. It was only gradually, as terrestrial food supplies developed, that amphibians began to explore the advantages of living on the land.

While amphibians achieved the peak of their development in the Carboniferous period, invertebrates flourished too, both on the land and in the water.

Insects, which originated in the Devonian, increased in number and size, encouraged by the warmth and rich vegetation of the Carboniferous. Dragonflies had a wingspread of 29 inches, crickets measured 10 inches, cockroaches were 4 inches long and grasshoppers were up to 1 foot long. Other familiar arthropods—scorpions, spiders, centipedes and millepedes—moved upon the land.

Foraminifers, bryozoans and echinoderms thrived in the warm Carboniferous seas. Brachiopods were present but declining. Corals, surprisingly, were inconspicuous.

Before the close of the Carboniferous, the decline of amphibian supremacy was being heralded by the appearance of the first reptiles—creatures far better adapted to life on the land. Known technically as cotylosaurs and popularly as "stem reptiles," they flourished into Permian time, branching out into a variety of lines. Typical of the stem reptiles was a small, homely, Texas-dwelling creature called *Seymouria,* half reptile and half amphibian in appearance.

The close of the Permian saw the widespread extinction of animal life, due to the period's chilling cold, suffocating dryness and the extensive withdrawal of the seas. Gone were the ruling trilobites, the eurypterids and many other marine invertebrates. Gone were the ostracoderms and placoderms, leaving fish evolution to the sharks and bony fishes. The chief survivors of the Permian upheaval were land animals and plants, and in the following Mesozoic Era the earth belonged to the reptiles.

Chapter 16 / The Mesozoic Era

The Mesozoic Era—the Era of Middle Life—began 225 million years ago and lasted 155 million years. It is divided into three periods: the Triassic (duration 45 million years), the Jurassic (45 million years) and the Cretaceous (65 million years).

This era is often called the Age of Reptiles, for it was during this time that enormous and grotesque reptilian forms dominated the animal kingdom. "Sea monsters" rode the ocean waves. Great flying reptiles swept through the skies. And in the North American West, millions of years before a cowboy galloped a horse into a sunset, the land trembled under the feet of dinosaurs.

GEOGRAPHY AND CLIMATE

The stable central interior of North America was surrounded, during the Mesozoic, by mountains and geosynclines on the East, South and West, and by the steadfast Canadian shield on the North.

The high, rugged Appalachian Mountains rose in the East.

The Ouachita Mountains, today a group of hills near the Arkansas-Oklahoma border, rimmed the interior on the South.

The Pacific Border geosyncline paralleled the North Pacific shore on the West.

The Mesocordilleran geanticline, a narrow sediment-supplying highland which extended from Alaska to Mexico, separated the Pacific geosyncline from the continent's western interior.

Eastward, the Rocky Mountain geosyncline paralleled the Mesocordilleran geanticline.

All these geographic divisions were affected by earth movements and the advances and withdrawals of the sea during the three periods of the Mesozoic.

In Triassic time the climate grew slowly less severe and the mountains built in the Permian period were gradually worn down. The seas encroached and retreated. Aridity was widespread in South America, western Europe, South Africa. Desert conditions prevailed in the West.

Toward the latter part of the Triassic, faulting occurred down a 1000-mile stretch between Nova Scotia and the Carolinas, resulting in a series of grabens bordered by block mountains. This faulting was accompanied by the extrusion of lava and the intrusion of dikes and sills. At the end of the Triassic these large blocks were broken and tilted, and the sills were exposed to erosion, as a result of an uplift in the region of the Appalachians. This earth movement, known as the Palisades orogeny, upturned the great sill which now forms the spectacular Palisades of the Hudson River.

In the early Jurassic, the Mesocordilleran geanticline served as a barricade against the moist winds moving inland from the Pacific. The result was continued aridity in the western interior section of North America. Later, however, the land subsided and ocean waters encroached, flooding the western half of the United States. Swamps developed in many places, and the climate became warm and damp.

Two new continental seas began to develop during the Jurassic. One came down from the Arctic Ocean and formed the Sundance Sea. The other established the beginnings of the Gulf of Mexico.

Late in the Jurassic, earth movements crumpled the Pacific geosyncline. At the same time, granitic magma invaded the sediments of California and British Columbia in large quantities. The great 16,000-square-mile Sierra Nevada batholith was intruded, and so was the Coast Range batholith—largest of all igneous masses at 73,000 square miles. This impressive display of crustal deformation and magmatic activity is called the Nevadan orogeny.

A monumental flooding of North America occurred during the Cretaceous. The lowlands sank, and the waters

crept inward from the Arctic Ocean and from the Gulf of
Mexico. Finally, in the middle of the period, a seaway up
to 1000 miles wide bisected the continent.

Large-scale flooding also occurred in other parts of
the world. Waters drowned the Sahara and broke up
Europe into islands. Almost all the main continental areas
of the earth were invaded.

The Cretaceous was one of the great chalk-forming
periods, too—in North America, northern France, and
England, where the White Cliffs of Dover were built.

As the period progressed, the crust of the earth grew
increasingly restless. Temperatures became colder. The
seas retreated from the continents.

The culmination of the period—a tremendous orogeny
known as the Laramide Revolution—lasted into the succeeding era and brought the Mesozoic to a close. It involved conspicuous vulcanism and intensive folding. In
North America the Rocky Mountain geosyncline became
the Rocky Mountains. In South America the Andes were
born. And in Central America the Antilles rose from the
sea.

PLANT LIFE

The plant life of the early Mesozoic was sparse and impov-
erished, for most of the lush Carboniferous vegetation had
vanished in the Permian crisis. In the latter part of the
Triassic the floras increased in number and variety, continuing with no major innovations into early Cretaceous
time.

Ferns were still represented by a number of groups.
The Paleozoic horsetails persisted, too, though they grew
considerably smaller than their predecessors.

The ginkgo tree appeared in the Mesozoic Era. This
native of the Orient, still growing today, has rounded pale-
green leaves.

Coniferous trees forested the land, some comparable
in size to the largest modern pines. Fabulous fossil conifers
of the Triassic can be seen today in Arizona's Petrified
Forest National Monument. The imposing sequoia of our
western forests had Mesozoic forebears.

The most characteristically Mesozoic plant was the slow-growing cycad, which came in hundreds of different varieties. Some were low, with a barrel-shaped, flower-covered trunk and a topping of palmy leaves. Some were tall and slim with spiral rows of leaf scars on the trunk, a crown of long and slender palmy leaves, and skinny flowers. Others had slender branching stems with flowers at the forks of the branches.

The flora of the earth was dramatically altered in mid-Cretaceous· time when the first angiosperms—flowering plants—appeared. These seed-encased plants probably originated in the tropics and then radiated into temperate regions. They were—and are—the highest form of life in the plant kingdom.

Fig, magnolia, poplar and sassafras trees were the first to establish themselves in the Cretaceous. Later came the birch, beech, sycamore, maple, oak, walnut and other deciduous trees. These angiosperms prospered and spread, brightening the land with color and giving it a strikingly modern aspect. They also provided a whole new food source—nuts, fruits, vegetables, grasses and cereals—for the more advanced animal forms that later took over the center of the stage.

ANIMAL LIFE

The marine invertebrate population of the Mesozoic was quite different from that of the preceding era, for many inhabitants of the Paleozoic seas failed to survive into the Triassic. The dominant forms were the mollusks, and the most distinctive mollusks were two now-extinct cephalopods—the ammonites and the belemnites.

Ammonites wore a single coiled thin and pearly shell, separated into two sections. There was a large forward chamber, occupied by the animal, and a gas-filled section divided by partitions called septa. Sizes ranged from diameters of 9 feet to only a few millimeters, and shapes varied from fat and tightly coiled to thin and loosely coiled. Paleozoic forms were modest, but in the Mesozoic they were lavishly ornamented with ribs, spines and other decorative features.

The ammonite, a now-extinct cephalopod, wore a single-coiled, thin, pearly shell, separated into two sections.

Belemnites resembled squids and, like their relatives, could discharge a fluid from an internal ink sac. Sometimes as long as 5 or 6 feet, belemnites wore a cigar-shaped calcium carbonate shell inside the body. These gregarious cephalopods traveled in groups, moving backward through the water in dart-like fashion.

Insects and other arthropods abounded in the Mesozoic. Most of the modern groups—grasshoppers, cockroaches, flies, dragonflies, termites, ants, moths and so forth—were represented.

Among the vertebrates were various fishes and amphibians. But throughout the Mesozoic Era the evolutionary spotlight was focused on the reptiles, which became the undisputed rulers of land, sea and air.

Why did the reptiles triumph over amphibians in the struggle for supremacy? Their great evolutionary advantage, back in the arid seasons of the late Paleozoic, was the development of a land egg. Where drought meant death to the eggs and young of a drying pond, total emancipation from the water had strong survival value.

Unlike the soft amphibian egg, the reptile's large, shelled egg could be laid directly on land because its shell prevented the air from drying it. Unlike the small amphibian egg, it contained a generous food supply in the yolk which supported the developing reptile. The young did not have to pass through an infantile stage in the water, but could remain in the egg until sufficiently developed to live comfortably on land.

By Triassic time, six separate reptile branches, called subclasses, had developed from cotylosaur ancestors.

1. One subclass of the great class Reptilia included the turtles, often described as the great "conservatives" of the reptile world. When they appeared in the middle of the Triassic, they probably couldn't tuck their necks into their shell for protection, as virtually all modern forms can do. Otherwise they resembled the turtles of today, and have persisted without change throughout the ages.

2. The mammal ancestors make up another subclass. An early member of this group was *Ophiacodon,* of late Paleozoic time. This primitive creature grew as long as 8 feet and had a long slim tail, pointed head and many

short teeth. It was probably a fish-eating reptile, inhabiting the banks of streams and ponds.

From such a creature evolved the weird-looking fin-backs of the late Paleozoic, distinguished by a row of long, upstanding spines that stood erect on the vertebral column and supported a connecting web of skin. This grotesque membranous sail of our ancient ancestors has long baffled paleontologists.

One picturesque theory is that the animal was partially aquatic and used its fin to sail in the prehistoric waters. Another unlikely suggestion is that it served to conceal the animal as it lay hidden among the rushes. Still another theory had it that the sail served no purpose at all and was merely a terrible inconvenience. Modern thinking on the subject, however, considers the sail a heat-regulating device which allowed both absorption and radiation.

Fin-backs included the carnivorous *Dimetrodon,* which had a large head and sharp teeth, and the plant-eating *Edaphosarus,* which had a large body, small head and small teeth.

From these pelycosaurs, as they were called, descended the therapsids, more direct mammal ancestors, with limbs that supported the body from beneath instead of sprawling out at the sides.

Cynognathus, a carnivorous therapsid representative of Triassic times, was about the size of a collie and justified its name of "dog jaw" by its well-developed incisor, canine and cheek teeth, which resembled those of mammals rather than reptiles. (The typical reptile has teeth of uniform size and shape. In *Cynognathus* they differed according to use.) Another Triassic reptile, *Ictidosaurus,* was even more mammal-like and was probably the link between reptiles and mammals.

3.   A third reptile subclass was made up of ichthyosaurs, which appeared in mid-Triassic and persisted throughout the Cretaceous. They became sea dwellers, more highly adapted to an aquatic environment than any other reptile group.

4.   The sauropterygians, members of a fourth subclass, returned to the sea too.

5.   In another subclass were the rhynchocephalians, currently represented by a small lizard-like animal called

Tyrannosaurus (right), the largest carnivore ever to walk the land, is seen attacking a *Triceratops*.

Sphenodon or the tuatara; the lizards, which appeared in the Triassic; and the snakes, which evolved from lizards, possibly in Cretaceous times.

The tuatara—a 2-foot, olive or brownish-yellow lizard-looking creature—is a living fossil now confined to a few isolated islands off the coast of New Zealand. Lizards and snakes, on the other hand, are the most abundant of the modern reptiles.

6.   The sixth branch consisted of Triassic thecodonts and the great number and variety of reptiles—some living and some now extinct—which descended from them. These included the flying reptiles (pterosaurs), the crocodilians (alligators and crocodiles) and, most spectacular of all, those monumental ruling reptiles—the dinosaurs.

Dinosaurs, a name meaning "terrible lizards," were present throughout the world. They made their first appearance in the Triassic and by the middle of that period outnumbered all the other reptiles put together. Starting out modestly at maximum lengths of 10–15 feet, many grew to giant proportions, small in brains but physically dwarfing all the other animals of their time.

There were two orders of dinosaurs—Ornithischia and Saurischia—divided according to the structure of their hip bones. All the ornithischians—the bird hips—were plant eaters, while the saurischians—the reptile hips—included not only herbivores but the fierce carnivores as well.

One of the best-known of the early saurischians was the sharp-toothed *Coelophysis* of late Triassic time. This hollow-boned meat eater weighed only 40–50 pounds, stood erect on its two hind legs and could run rapidly to pounce on prey or escape from enemies.

Several other erect carnivores stalked the earth in the Jurassic period. There was the 24-foot-long *Ceratosaurus,* equipped with a bony horn on its nose, and *Ornitholestes,* small, light and graceful, with a slender tail, slim bird-like legs and short grasping arms. There was the cat-sized *Compsognathus,* graceful and delicate, and the sharp-toothed, sharp-clawed *Allosaurus,* a ferocious predator 30 feet in length.

In Cretaceous times appeared the bipedal *Ornithomimus,* an ostrich-like saurischian whose name means "ostrich mimic." It had long slender legs and neck, a small head and toothless bird-like jaws which it used to feed on insects and fruit and to suck the eggs of other dinosaurs.

The Cretaceous period was distinguished by the presence of the largest carnivore to ever walk the land. This was the terrifying *Tyrannosaurus,* which stood nearly 20 feet tall and measured 50 feet from its nose to the tip of its long heavy tail. The massive body, which weighed from 8 to 10 tons, was carried erect by stout, muscular, clawed hind legs and was topped by a great head studded with murderous teeth. The dwarfed front legs were utterly out of proportion to the rest of the animal's awesome body.

All the erect carnivores belonged to a saurischian subdivision called the theropods. The other important saurischians walked on four legs and were amphibious and herbivorous. These sauropods, as they were called, included the largest land animals of all time.

Probably the most familiar of the sauropods was *Brontosaurus,* whose neck and tail seemed to extend indefinitely. This huge but relatively gentle beast measured 80 feet from tip to tip, weighed some 40 tons and had thick legs, a snaky neck and a startlingly small head. In approximately the same weight and length category were two near relatives, *Brachiosaurus* (heavier—50 tons) and Diplodocus—(longer—87½ feet).

These massive reptiles lived in regions where the Rocky Mountains and high plains of Utah, Colorado and Wyoming now stand. In the Jurassic, however, these were lowlands—with swamps and lagoons and rich vegetation. *Brontosaurus* and its relatives probably spent most of their life in the lagoons, where the water's buoyancy helped them to carry their great weight. The lagoon also offered safety from predatory land-dwelling carnivores.

Although the saurischians included the largest of the dinosaurs, the herbivorous ornithischians surely included some of the strangest-looking: duck-billed, plated, armored and horned.

Ancestor of all these forms was the Jurassic bipedal *Camptosaurus,* whose bird-like beak and flattened, blade-like teeth adapted for eating plants were typical of most of the order. *Iguanodon,* a similar type, was sometimes more than 30 feet long. It was distinguished by a spiky thumb which appeared on each fore limb.

The duck-bills (also called hadrosaurs), with their duck-like beaks and webbed feet, appeared in Cretaceous times. They walked erect on massive limbs, but lowered themselves to all fours to dine on the rushes beside streams. Many of them could swim. Among the duck-bills were *Trachodon,* most common of the group, the 25-foot-long *Anatosaurus;* and the crested *Parasaurolophus* and *Corythosaurus.*

The four-legged ornithischians were represented in Jurassic time by the 10-ton *Stegosaurus,* a plated dinosaur with a small head, a brain the size of a kitten's and a huge body. The rear legs were considerably longer than the front, giving the beast a weird humpbacked appearance. Two rows of large, triangular plates marched down its spine, and four fierce spikes adorned its tail.

These protective devices were elaborated on in Cretaceous times by *Ankylosaurus,* an armored dinosaur whose broad, squat body was not only totally plated but equipped with projecting spikes along each side from front to rear. Its tail was tipped with a knobby bone, which served as an effective club.

Also present in the Cretaceous period were the horned dinosaurs, known as ceratopsians. These included small (6 feet long) *Protoceratops,* which wore a shield-like structure of bone over its neck, and the 20–30-foot-long *Triceratops,* with a large flaring shield on its neck and three great head horns—two over the eyes and one on the nose.

Other similar late Cretaceous forms included one with a big horn on the nose, a small horn above the eyes and a modest frill. Another had a frill like that of *Triceratops,* bordered by large horns. This well-protected beast wore, in addition, a pair of small horns above the eyes and a large horn on the nose.

While the dinosaurs ruled the land, representatives of all but one of the reptile subclasses returned to the sea and became masters of that domain. Since evolution does not go backward, they could not simply regress to a former fish-like condition. Instead, they had to modify their land-adapted features to take to the waters again.

Crocodilian members of the ruling reptiles were well-adapted to marine life in Jurassic times. Their limbs served as steering paddles, and they were equipped with fish-like tails.

From the turtle subclass came the giant sea turtles, including the huge *Protostega,* and the even huger *Archelon. Archelon* had a parrot-like beak, measured more than 12 feet and probably weighed a full 3 tons.

Ichthyosaurs, which made their first appearance in mid-Triassic times, lived a watery existence throughout the Jurassic and Cretaceous. They resembled dolphins or porpoises, with a talent for rapid swimming and impressive leaps into the air. The ichthyosaur's muscular, streamlined body—perhaps as long as 25 feet—had the tail of a fish and fins instead of limbs. Its eyes were big and its jaws full of sharp teeth.

Because ichthyosaurs were built like fish, they could not lay their eggs on land. And yet a reptile egg will drown if it is laid in water. How did ichthyosaurs reproduce? Perhaps, it has been suggested, these reptile young were born alive in the ocean.

The heavy-bodied, short-necked placodonts and the slim long-necked nothosaurs were marine reptiles of the sauropterygian group. They lived during Triassic times and were followed, in the Jurassic and Cretaceous periods, by the considerably more fearsome plesiosaurs, described as "a snake threaded through the shell of a turtle."

Many plesiosaurs were only 12–20 feet long, but the giants among them—*Kronosaurus* is an example—measured almost 50 feet in length. Most had a broad, flat, bone-plated trunk and a long flexible neck ending in a small head which could maneuver rapidly to catch fish. *Elasmosaurus,* for instance, had a neck that was twice the length of the body and contained 60 vertebrae. Plesiosaurs rowed through the waters on paddle-like limbs and snapped up their prey with sharp-toothed jaws.

The lizards produced, in Cretaceous time, another version of the sea monster—the up-to-30-foot-long mosasaur. This scaly-skinned creature had a slim, elongated body and a tapering tail. With its powerful jaws and vicious teeth, it was the most rapacious of the Mesozoic marine vertebrates.

Having established their hegemony over land and sea, the reptiles went on to conquer the air. Until the Mesozoic

Ichthyosaurs resembled dolphins or porpoises, with a talent for rapid swimming and impressive leaps into the air.

Era, insects were the only form of air-born life, but in the Jurassic period a group of featherless flying reptiles called pterosaurs became the first vertebrates to take to the sky.

Like the dinosaurs, pterosaurs had thecodont ancestors, but their pattern of evolution was entirely different from that of their land-bound relations. In pterosaurs, the rear limbs became smaller and the breastbone and fore-limbs grew stronger. One finger extended outward in dramatically elongated fashion, and from it and the entire arm a piece of membrane stretched back to the body, forming a primitive bat-like wing. The other three fingers were used for clinging.

Among the earliest pterosaurs was *Rhamphorhynchus,* which was 3 feet long, with a short body and a very long tail terminating in a diamond-shaped membrane which served as a rudder. Its hind legs were slim and feeble, its front legs strong. Its long beak contained sharp forward-pointing teeth which were probably used to snatch fish from the surface of the water.

Another flying reptile of the Jurassic period was *Pterodactylus*. It ranged from sparrow size to hawk size, had a very small tail and was equipped with sharp teeth.

In the Cretaceous period appeared the great *Pteranodon,* the largest flying creature of all time. Although its tiny-tailed body was merely the size of a holiday turkey, its huge wings darkened the air with a spread of 27 feet. Instead of a jaw full of teeth it had a long, toothless, bird-like beak. A bony crest of almost the same length projected back from the skull.

As early as the mid-Jurassic the pterosaurs were sharing the skies with *Archaeopteryx,* the earliest known bird. (It did not evolve from flying reptiles, but both had a common ancestor.) Midway between reptile and bird, *Archaeopteryx* showed its thecodont ancestry in its sharp reptilian teeth, clawed wings and long bony tail. But unlike any reptile that had ever before appeared, it wore a unique body covering—feathers.

In the Cretaceous period, other bird types appeared. One was the flightless *Hesperornis,* a water-dwelling diver. Another was *Ichthyornis,* which lived like a tern and had powerful wings.

It was the descendants of the Mesozoic birds that

ultimately became possessors of the sky, for when the era came to a close 70 million years ago, it took with it all the winged reptiles. The era's end also saw the extermination of the reptilian monsters of the seas. And on land the great and glorious dinosaurs vanished forever, victims, like the others, of forces no one yet fully understands.

Did the climate become too cold? Did the dinosaurs grow too big? Were the herbivores unable to adjust to a change of diet when new plant forms appeared? Did the early mammals devour the dinosaur eggs? Even if the answers are yes, they do not explain the mass extermination in tropical climates, or why the small-sized dinosaurs vanished, or a number of other baffling facts. Perhaps, some scientists have suggested, these reptile races died of old age, just as individuals do, after a rich full life of millions upon millions of years.

Whatever the causes, the great Mesozoic reptiles were gone. The only survivors of the class Reptilia were those that still exist today—the turtles, lizards, snakes, crocodiles and rhynchocephalians. But none of these dominated the earth during the following era. The land power passed to a class of small, unobtrusive creatures which had managed to elude the mighty carnivores. The Age of Reptiles had given way to the Age of Mammals.

Chapter 17 / The Cenozoic Era

The Age of Mammals is more formally called the Cenozoic Era. It began 70 million years ago and has not yet come to an end. During this relatively brief span of geologic time our planet's face acquired the features we know today, modern plant forms spread across the earth, and the animal kingdom produced its most distinguished mammal, *Homo sapiens*.

The Cenozoic is divided into two periods and then further subdivided into seven epochs. The Tertiary period lasted from 70 million to 1 million years ago and included five epochs: Paleocene (70–60 million), Eocene (60–40 million), Oligocene (40–25 million), Miocene (25–11 million) and Pliocene (11–1 million). The Quaternary period is composed of the Pleistocene epoch of about a million years' duration, and the following Recent epoch, in which we are living today. (Note: Although the Pleistocene is still given as an epoch of about one million years, keep in mind that geologists now believe it may have been two or more million.)

GEOGRAPHY AND CLIMATE

Early in the Cenozoic, the Atlantic coastal plain between Long Island and Florida was partly submerged. So were the landward margins of the Pacific and the Gulf of Mexico. But aside from a narrow seaway which penetrated the Dakotas from the Gulf in Paleocene time, there were no extensive inland seas occupying the continent. Following the Paleocene, invading waters all over the world gradually decreased, until the modern boundaries between continents and seas were established.

The physiography of our continent as we know it today was produced during the Cenozoic. Diastrophism was of major significance, but earth movements which involved downwarping and upwarping were more extensive than those which produced folds and faults.

At the beginning of the Tertiary, the Appalachians—except for the Great Smokies and scattered New England peaks—were reduced to a low-lying plain. Over the course of the era these already highly folded mountains underwent successive phases of uplift and erosion and were eventually carved to their present shape by geologic agents.

West of the Appalachians, the rocks of the interior form a lowland. Beyond stretch the Great Plains, extending, roughly, from the Mississippi to the Rockies. During the Cenozoic, this region remained undisturbed by orogeny, as it had since the end of Precambrian time.

The Rocky Mountains stood high when the Cenozoic began, but in the ensuing epochs they were cut down by erosion. Sediments from the mountains were deposited in broad basins that lay between the peaks. By the Oligocene the filled basins and planed mountains formed a low monotonous region. In the Miocene this region was uplifted, then sculpted by rejuvenated streams. Thus the essential structure of the Rockies is due to the folding which occurred during the Laramide orogeny, while their present topography is the result of stream erosion in the late Cenozoic.

The Colorado Plateau of the American Southwest experienced uplift after uplift during the Cenozoic Era. One of the streams rejuvenated by vertical movement was the Colorado River, which carved the glorious mile-deep Grand Canyon, perhaps beginning its work in late Pliocene time. Although the Colorado Plateau is surrounded by folded and deformed rock, the rocks of the Plateau itself are virtually horizontal. The great gash of the Grand Canyon reveals layer after layer of these sedimentary beds, providing a sweeping look into the earth's geological past.

The Basin and Range province, a region of isolated mountain ranges separated by desert plains and basins, developed during the Cenozoic in parts of Nevada, Utah, Oregon, Idaho, Arizona, New Mexico, Texas, California and northern Mexico. The ranges are uplifted blocks of pre-Cenozoic rock that were elevated along fault planes in Miocene time.

Fissure eruptions of basaltic lava occurred during the Cenozoic Era, with great quantities accumulating over many thousands of square miles between the northern Rockies and the Cascade Ranges. After the main outpouring of lava, the region was uplifted. It is known today as the Columbia Plateau, a warped upland standing at elevations of 3000 to over 8000 feet.

The long stretch of western mountains formed by the Sierra Nevada and Cascades, the farther-west ridges of the Coast Ranges, and the broad basin separating the two parallel belts are—in large measure—the product of Cenozoic diastrophism.

The Sierra Nevada consists of an enormous tilted fault block, about 100 miles wide and 400 miles long. The block is a portion of the huge granitic batholith which was intruded into the region back in Jurassic time. Erosion stripped the rocks above the batholith during the Cretaceous and early Tertiary. Then, late in the Cenozoic, momentous earth movements tilted it westward. Volcanism and diastrophism raised the mountain to its present elevation, about 13,000 feet. The appearance of the Sierra Nevada, which blocks the rain-bearing winds traveling east from the Pacific, helped bring the southwestern desert into being.

The Cascades are a series of volcanoes built on the western side of the Columbia Plateau during the Pleistocene. Major peaks include Shasta (14,161 feet), Rainier (14,408), Hood (11,253) and Baker (10,750). The Cascades' Lassen Peak (10,453), which erupted in 1914 and 1915, is the only volcano known to be active within the contiguous United States. But several other volcanic peaks may be merely dormant rather than extinct.

Along the Pacific the Coast Ranges experienced uplift throughout the Cenozoic. Their greatest vertical movement occurred in the mid-Pleistocene.

On other continents during the Cenozoic, the Andes were eroded and then uplifted, while the Alps and Himalayas were raised from the bottom of the sea by the compression of the land masses on either side. The Pyrenees, Apennines and Carpathians were also among the important mountain ranges created by Cenozoic diastrophism. World-wide vulcanism during this era culminated in the striking "ring of fire" which borders the Pacific Ocean.

The climate of the Cenozoic was initially warm and moist, but it chilled as the epochs wore on. The cooling weather culminated, in Pleistocene time, with the advent of the Great Ice Age.

There had been many ice ages earlier in earth's history, but what is known as the Great Ice Age began a million years ago, in the areas near the poles and on high mountain tops where snow fell and did not melt. On our continent, ice amassed in the north, forming huge sheets that spread down into North America, glaciating nearly 6 million square miles of land. Four times, it is believed, enormous growths of ice occurred and glaciers moved across the land. Four times the glaciers melted and retreated.

Among the many theories seeking to explain the causes of glacial climate are three of particular interest.

One proposes that the carbon dioxide, water vapor and dust of earth's atmosphere create a "greenhouse effect" by retaining the heat from solar radiation close to the surface of the earth. A reduction in these constituents of the atmosphere might have caused the climate to cool in Pleistocene time.

Reduction of the amount of energy emitted by the sun could also produce a glacial climate, a second theory proposes. Unfortunately there is no known way to determine whether a significant drop in the sun's energy output occurred during the Great Ice Age.

A third theory emphasizes the role of cosmic dust. If a dense cloud of this material screened out a significant portion of the sun's energy in Pleistocene time, the earth would have chilled. This is an intriguing theory, but no one yet knows how it can be tested.

Although the causes of the Great Ice Age are unknown, its effects are apparent everywhere. (See Chapter 8.) As the glaciers advanced, forests were erased, mountains and valleys were reshaped, parts of the land were scoured bare and other parts were enriched with new deposits of soil. As they melted, glacial deposits—ridges, hills, terrraces and plains—were left behind.

Sea levels rose as glaciers retreated, and fell as they advanced. When the sea level was low, Britain and Ireland were joined to Europe, and Ceylon and India were connected. Many of the islands of Indonesia were joined, to each other and to the Asian mainland. The Old World and the New were linked by a land bridge across the Bering Strait, permitting the westward migration of zebras, camels and horses, and the eastward migration of elephants, elks and man.

PLANT LIFE

Modern plant life extended its domain throughout the world during the Cenozoic. In western America the subtropical climate that characterized early Cenozoic times fostered the growth of plants like breadfruit and palmettos. As far north as Alaska, magnolia and fig trees bloomed. Osage oranges, pawpaws and locust trees grew near Toronto. But as the climate cooled, these warm-weather plants retreated to the southlands.

The most significant event of the era occurred in the cooler, drier Miocene epoch, when grasses suddenly spread over huge areas of land, creating the world's plains, prairies and veldts. The importance of these grasses—the most widely distributed of the flowering plants—cannot be overestimated. They serve as a food for almost all grazing animals, and from them a number of domesticated grasses (wheat, rice, barley and corn) are derived. In addition, their presence is crucial in controlling erosion.

During the Great Ice Age, much plant life was buried by the glaciers' advance. But each time the more temperate climate of the interglacial periods reappeared, the plants reappeared too. Today they flourish everywhere—high on the mountains and far below sea level, in the unkind aridity of the desert and in regions of ceaseless rains.

ANIMAL LIFE

Soon after the beginning of the Cenozoic Era, marine invertebrates attained their modern forms. The basic bird structure, highly evolved by the end of the Mesozoic, showed only subtle alterations through the Cenozoic, except for the development of very large flightless birds like the frightful, 7-foot-high *Diatryma,* with a skull and beak measuring 1½ feet long, and powerful scaly legs and claws. The reptiles that survived the Cretaceous period were much the same as those that now exist. It was the mammals that underwent the most drastic changes, to become the dominant form of life on earth today.

There are several characteristics which have enabled mammals to achieve their evolutionary success.

1. Because they are warm-blooded and can maintain an even body temperature, they are capable of coping with variations in climate. Reptiles, which are cold-blooded, become immobilized in cold weather and suffer from heat stroke when the weather is hot. Thus their geographic range is restricted, while mammals can wander far and wide.

2. The mammal brain is highly developed, particularly the centers of memory and intelligence. Vertebrate intelligence is correlated with the convolutions of the brain's cerebral hemispheres and the amount of "gray matter" spread over its surface. In reptiles the cerebral hemispheres are relatively unimportant. In birds the hemispheres are large, but there is little gray matter. Mammals have both large hemispheres and a great deal of gray matter.

3. With few exceptions, mammals give birth to living young, nurse them and provide them with a long period of postnatal care and training. It is believed that these reproductive habits relate to the need for the slow, safe development of complex mechanisms like the brain.

Despite these and many other excellent qualifications, mammals did not achieve mastery until the extinction of the ruling reptiles. They began as small forest dwellers, later increasing in size and spreading throughout the world.

Three major categories of mammals exist today—monotremes, marsupials and placentals. Most primitive are the monotremes, whose ancestors were probably present back in Triassic times and who are currently represented by only two Australian types—the platypus (a toothless swimmer and digger with a broad horny bill) and the spiny anteater (with a long slim snout and powerful digging feet). Although monotremes—like all mammals—nurse their young, they reproduce—like the reptiles—by laying eggs.

The first marsupial mammals appeared later in the Mesozoic. They were once widespread and abundant, but now thrive only on the island continent of Australia, which seems to have been isolated since Cretaceous time. Some opossum representatives are found in North and South America.

Marsupial mothers give birth to tiny, immature young after a short period of gestation. The baby marsupial must then be protected and nourished in an external pouch on its mother's belly until it is able to cope with the world. Typical modern marsupials are the kangaroo and the opossum. Both are born with well-developed front limbs which permit them to climb up to the pouch or "marsupium."

Placental mammals have the most efficient method of reproduction—the mother carries her young safely inside the uterus until it has achieved a relatively advanced stage of development. This prebirth nurturing has given placentals the evolutionary edge ever since Cretaceous times, when their small insectivore ancestors (today represented by shrews, hedgehogs and moles) appeared on the scene. The following brief look at Cenozoic mammals will be focused entirely on placentals, which include 95% of known mammalian forms.

In Paleocene times, first epoch of the Tertiary period of the Cenozoic Era, archaic mammals roamed the land. Among them were the carnivorous creodonts—long-bodied, long-tailed and short-limbed, not very fast or very intelligent. Also present were the herbivorous condylarths and unitatheres, both primitive ungulates (primarily mammals with hoofs). The condylarths resembled creodonts in general appearance but had teeth adapted for eating plants, and a hoof capping each toe. The unitatheres, grotesque rhinoceros-sized creatures with six horn-like knobs atop their heads, were the largest land animals of Eocene times.

By the end of the Eocene epoch, the archaic mammals had become extinct, supplanted by ancestors of our present-day mammals. The ungulates, which include almost all the larger herbivores, separated into two basic types—the odd-toed and the even-toed.

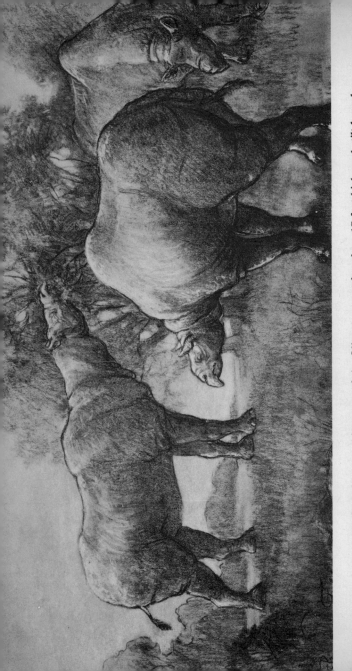

The *Baluchitherium*, rhinoceros of the Oligocene, was hornless, 17 feet high, and stilt-legged.

Perissodactyls—the odd-toed ungulates—are represented by horses and their relatives (zebras and asses), tapirs and rhinoceroses and two extinct groups, the titanotheres and the chalicotheres. The most detailed mammalian fossil .ecords, from tiny *Eohippus* to modern *Equus,* have been left by the horse.

Eohippus, the dawn horse of Eocene times, was slim and fox-terrier-sized, with four toes in front and three in back. As it evolved it lost toes, increased in size and developed high-crowned teeth suitable for chewing the hard grasses of the plains. By the beginning of the Pleistocene, the modern one-toed *Equus* had appeared in North America, surviving throughout the Great Ice Age, then vanishing until the Spanish conquerors reintroduced horses to this continent.

Tapirs and rhinoceroses were also one-time residents of North America. The modern tapir exhibits many characteristics of the Eocene horse, like low-crowned teeth and the same distribution of toes on front and rear feet. The rhinoceros has produced some interesting forms during its evolutionary history: the slender, horse-like creature of the Eocene; the hornless, 17-foot-high, stilt-legged *Baluchitherium* of the Oligocene; and the woolly rhinoceros of the Ice Age.

The titanotheres, confined almost exclusively to North America, were slow, elephantine and horned. The chalicotheres were horse-like in appearance but wore, instead of hoofs, great claws at the ends of their feet.

The perissodactyls were quite successful in the early part of the Cenozoic, but as the era progressed their numbers decreased. Meanwhile the even-toed ungulates, the artiodactyls, became ever more important and are, today, the most common and widespread mammals in existence.

The first even-toed types appeared early in the Eocene epoch and were almost from the beginning divided into two groups—the pigs and their relations, and the cud-chewers or ruminants. The first group is composed of pigs and peccaries, which appeared in the Oligocene, and the hippopotamuses of Pliocene times. The ruminants are distinguished by a complicated, usually four-chambered stomach which allows food to be eaten rapidly, regurgitated, then chewed and digested in more leisurely fashion. Living

The first mastodons appeared in early Oligocene times.

ruminants include camels and llamas, the earliest group to develop; mouse deer, tiny browsers of the Old World tropics; deer; giraffes; pronghorns; and bison, sheep, goats, antelopes and cattle.

Although these odd- and even-toed types are the most important ungulates, they are by no means the only ones. Another interesting group, the subungulates, includes the rodent-like conies of Africa and Syria, the sea cows and the proboscidians (mammals with trunks), whose only living representative is the elephant. Small, pig-sized proboscidians were present in the late Eocene. They were followed in early Oligocene times by the first mastodons, later represented in this country by *Mastodon americanus*. The true elephants of Pleistocene times, known as mammoths, were almost world-wide in distribution. A northern variety, the woolly mammoth, was guarded from the cold by a covering of shaggy hair.

Significant ungulate evolution also occurred in South America, which remained an isolated island continent for most of the Tertiary period. But the South American story, with its many colorful characters, must wait for another book. It is time to leave the ungulates for a look at the other groups of Cenozoic mammals.

At the end of the Eocene and the start of the Oligocene, the creodonts were replaced by modern flesh eaters, the fissipeds. These carnivores are divided into two great land groups, one including dogs and their relatives (weasels, skunks, badgers, otters, raccoons, bears, dogs, wolves and foxes); the other including cats and their relatives (civets, hyenas, house cats, lions, tigers, cougars, bobcats and so forth). The pinnipeds—marine carnivores—comprise a third group of flesh eaters. They dine primarily on fish and include seals, sea lions and walruses.

Besides ungulates and carnivores there are a variety of other mammalian forms which reached their present evolutionary stage during the Cenozoic: the gnawing rodents (squirrels, beavers, rats, mice, porcupines, guinea pigs and others), most flourishing of all mammals; the hares and rabbits, also gnawers; bats, the only air-borne mammals; whales, porpoises and dolphins; and edentates, "toothless" mammals centered chiefly in South America. But of primary importance to us is the group, or order, called the primates, chiefly arboreal creatures which include tree shrews, lemurs, tarsiers, monkeys, apes and man.

Tree shrews, most primitive of the primates, are squirrel-sized insect eaters with long bushy tails and pointed snouts. The lemurs, next in the evolutionary hierarchy, are heavily covered with fur and have pointed snouts, large pointed ears, a long tail, and hands and feet well-adapted for grasping. Probable bridge between lemur and monkey was a primate group from which sprung the tarsier, a tiny nocturnal tree dweller with a reduced nose and enormous eyes, a long rat-like tail and long hind legs.

Ancestors of the shrews, lemurs and tarsiers were present in Paleocene and Eocene times. The monkeys and apes made their appearance in mid-Cenozoic, each line originating independently from the tarsiers.

Monkeys are divided into two groups—Old World and South American monkeys. Although the Old World forms are more advanced, in both groups the eyes are set close together in front of the head, permitting stereoscopic vision; the hands are used for grasping objects; the brain is comparatively large. The anthropoid or man-like apes have four types of living representatives—gibbons, smallest and most primitive of the apes; chimpanzees, slightly smaller than man, but very powerful; orangutans, red-haired and approximately the size of a man; and gorillas, about 6 feet tall but much heavier than man. Two of these, the chimp and the gorilla, lead a more-or-less ground existence and have a human-type mentality. Although neither of these anthropoids is man's direct ancestor, they almost surely belong to the group from which man has descended.

THE PLEISTOCENE EPOCH

Known occurrences of fossil man are so scattered and so rare that our present classifications must be regarded as tentative. New discoveries about man's ancestry continue to be made, pushing his history further back into the past.

The story of man's evolution is set in the Pleistocene epoch, which began at least a million years ago and perhaps as far back as two million. It was a time of drastic climatic changes, and the demands of "adjust or die" were never more severe. The advance of glaciers turned tropics into pine forests and, finally, into stark tundra lands. With the retreat of the glaciers the process was reversed, and ice-locked regions became green and mild once again. As the zones of plant life shifted back and forth, so did many groups of animals. Others developed adaptations to the cold. Still others—those who failed to migrate and could not adjust—perished.

Most of the animal forms that live on our continent today roamed our forests and plains during the Great Ice Age. So did many other creatures that are now extinct or restricted to other parts of the world.

There were 9-foot-high mastodons, lions, horses and camels, and hordes of musk oxen, bison and deer. There were woolly rhinoceroses garbed in long, shaggy coats to withstand the cold, and woolly mammoths—domeheaded, humpbacked and also warmly dressed—whose perfectly preserved carcasses have been found in the frozen tundra of Siberia and Alaska. There was *Smilodon,* a saber-toothed cat larger and heavier than the modern tiger and capable of attacking the huge, thick-skinned mastodons with its long, curved, saber-like upper teeth.

Mammals grew to gigantic proportions in the Great Ice Age. Beavers were as big as bears. Ground sloths were heavier than the modern elephant. In Australia the kangaroos stood 10 feet tall.

In this country fascinating fossil remains of many Pleistocene creatures accumulated in the La Brea tar pits of Los Angeles. These dank depressions, covered with a thin film of water, attracted thirsty Ice Age animals which were then fatally trapped in the thick gummy ooze.

Among the multitude of mammals that left fossil records throughout the world during this epoch was a South African creature called *Australopithecus,* a name meaning "southern ape." Most of its features—the massive, protruding jaw, low forehead and prominent brow ridges— were clearly ape-like. But its teeth showed many human characteristics, its skull was a little closer to the human skull and its brain was proportionately large for its 4-foot height. *Australopithecus* walked erect, dwelt on the ground, made very crude tools and possibly used fire.

Following *Australopithecus* came a more advanced

Perhaps 250,000 years ago, perhaps even earlier, the Neanderthal man occupied a large part of the world—France, Italy, Germany, Iran, northern Africa and other areas.

type *Homo habilis,* with a larger brain capacity. Evidence indicates that he was capable of making better tools than his predecessor. His name, suggested by noted paleontologist Dr. Raymond Dart, means "able, handy, mentally skillful and vigorous."

Later along in the Pleistocene appeared *Pithecanthropus* and *Sinanthropus,* more popularly known as Java man and Peking man. *Pithecanthropus* had heavy, ape-like brow ridges, a broad face and flattened nose and a brain considerably smaller than that of modern man. Yet the contours of the brain were basically human in arrangement, as were the arrangement of the teeth. Primitive creature though he was, *Pithecanthropus* was clearly man, not ape. So was *Sinanthropus,* who closely resembled Java man and was a maker of tools and a user of fire. Much to the distress of fastidious geologists, Peking man also appears to have been something of a cannibal, for fossil remains consist of broken skulls whose brains have been removed.

Perhaps 250,000 years ago, perhaps even earlier, Neanderthal man (*Homo neanderthalensis*) occupied a large part of the world—France, Italy, Germany, Iran, northern Africa and other areas. His face was stamped with the look of the ape (low forehead, prominent brow ridges); his body was short (about 5 feet 4 inches), stocky and stooped. He had long arms, a barrel-like chest, a powerful jaw and receding chin. He was probably quite furry. Unprepossessing, indeed quite brutish in appearance, Neanderthal was nevertheless distinguished by the presence of a large brain, which set him far above the *Pithecanthropus* level. He had learned to build a fire, to fashion stone weapons and—most significantly—to bury his dead.

Near the end of the Pleistocene, Neanderthal man became extinct, supplanted by a new group of men who appeared in Europe. These were the Cro-Magnons, of the genus and species *Homo sapiens.* Tall, ruggedly built and handsome, with a high forehead and long skull, Cro-magnon man had an appearance so modern that he would not look out of place in the twentieth century. The magnificent paintings he left on the walls of his caves—at Altamira, Spain, and Lascaux, France—tell, much better than any words, just how far life had advanced since its mindless, microscopic beginning back when the world was young.

Chapter 18 / Geology and Man

Man's progress along the path of civilization is, in important measure, the story of his mastery of earth's minerals and rocks. In the early stages of his history, man chipped away at flint and put to use the primitive stone implements he formed. Today the entire assemblage of this planet's mineral riches—utilized in a host of sophisticated ways—is at his disposal.

Minerals now provide him with the iron, copper, aluminum and other metals vital to an industrial civilization. Coal and petroleum serve as his chief sources of power. From the earth come the bricks that build his houses and the asphalt that forms his streets, the salt for his food and the precious gems and metals for his pleasure and profit. The wealth and power of his nation are, to a large extent, determined by its possession and exploitation of the minerals of the earth.

THE AGES OF MAN

The physical evolution of man can be traced through his fossil remains. His cultural evolution can be traced through the implements and other objects associated with these fossils. The sequence of cultures represented by man's weapons and tools are known as "ages." They are not discrete periods of time but, rather, stages of development which may be achieved by different people at different times.

The first phase of man's cultural history began in the Pleistocene with the Stone Age and ended with the discovery of metals, which took place about 3500 B.C. in the Middle East. On our continent, the American Indians were, for the most part, still in the Stone Age when Columbus arrived in 1492.

The Stone Age may be divided into old (Paleolithic), middle (Mesolithic) and new (Neolithic). The implements associated with Stone Age cultures were of two general types. There were hand axes and other tools formed by a core of flint from which chips were removed. And there were flake tools, formed of flakes struck from the core. Massive choppers of the core-tool variety were associated with *Sinanthropus* and *Pithecanthropus,* while more sophisticated implements, including bone needles, were fashioned by Cro-Magnon man.

Separated by the transition years of the Mesolithic, the New Stone Age contrasts sharply with the Old. New Stone Age man learned to polish and grind his implements, so that he could utilize not only flint but all sorts of igneous rocks. He devised pottery, which enormously improved water- and food-storage facilities. He wove flax and used the cloth to fashion fishing nets. And, most important, he domesticated animals and developed agriculture.

No longer was man a nomadic hunter, wandering wherever the food supply led. He lived in a community now, working out his private destiny within the boundaries of a settled social setting. In Mesopotamia, early Neolithic culture was present in 5000 B.C., and probably even earlier. Well-established Neolithic villages were widespread in the Near East by 4000 B.C. Development was slower in Europe, where agricultural villagers did not replace wandering hunters until after 3000 B.C.

The Metal Ages—bronze and then iron—followed the Neolithic. Copper was first used alone, then combined with tin to form the more powerful alloy bronze. By about 3500 B.C. the discovery of founding or casting was established in the Near East and a Bronze Age had begun. Soon bronze was used for ornaments and took the place of stone in weapons and tools. By 2000 B.C. this metal was common throughout most of Europe.

The development of metallurgy—mining, smelting and casting—was accompanied by the rise of urbanization, the specialization of labor, and the production of surplus foods to support an artisan class. In the search for raw materials, new regions were explored and colonized, and extensive trade routes were opened. Transportation was facilitated by the creation of the wheeled vehicle and the sail. Writing was invented. Science arose, and the institutions of state and church became established.

On the heels of the Bronze Age came the Iron Age, well underway in Asia, Egypt and Europe in the first millennium before Christ. During the period between 1900 and 1400 B.C., smelted iron ornaments and ceremonial weapons were in common use. Then the Hittites invented tempering, and in the following centuries other civilizations swiftly acquired a knowledge of iron technology. Not until the Industrial Revolution of the nineteenth century, however, was the casting of iron technically useful.

The basic innovations of the Bronze Age were developed by the people who lived in the Age of Iron. Travel became faster and farther-ranging. Reading and writing sifted down from the scribe to the common man. The invention of money increased the flow of commerce. Theoretical science was advanced. Social institutions grew ever more complex. And the Greeks invented written history, which has continued man's story down to the present day.

EARTH'S MINERAL WEALTH

With each succeeding phase of human history, man has become increasingly dependent on earth's mineral resources. Today they are second only to agriculture in importance.

Mineral Fuels   The most important mineral resources are the mineral fuels—coal, petroleum and natural gas. (Others, the so-called nuclear fuels, are now being developed.) Coal, well-known as a crucial industrial fuel, also provides a large number of valuable chemical products— ammonia, dyes, perfumes, flavors, antiseptics, aspirin and other drugs. It is still the basic fuel of industrialized nations, supplying the world with more energy than oil and gas put together. However, petroleum, originally a kerosene source, is today vitally important in transportation. And natural gas is being used in greater and greater amounts in power plants and metallurgy.

Coal is a black or blackish-brown rock that burns. It forms beds anywhere from a fraction of an inch to many feet thick, and is composed of the compressed and chemically changed remains of land plants. Coal develops from a slightly modified plant residue called peat, through lignite and bituminous coal, to hard black anthracite. An estimate of the world's total coal reserves is the awe-inspiring figure of more than seven trillion tons, with the United States boasting about 60% of this total. Most of America's high-rank coal comes from West Virginia, Pennsylvania, Kentucky, Illinois and Ohio. Other important deposits of coal are found in China, Russia, Australia, Great Britain and France.

Natural gas, petroleum (oil), and asphalt form a series of what are called hydrocarbons. Hydrocarbons are compounds made up, chiefly, of the elements hydrogen and carbon. Those with a few carbon atoms form natural gas, those with a larger number form petroleum. Those with a great number of carbon atoms form asphalt or paraffin.

Petroleum and natural gas are almost always found in sedimentary rocks, particularly in sandstone. The oil occupies the spaces between rock grains and is brought to the surface of the earth by drilling wells. The oil may flow to the surface naturally, but more commonly it must be pumped.

Most petroleum appears to have originated as organic materials which accumulated in sediments deposited on the floor of the sea. Such oil-producing sediments are known as source rocks. The process seems to require a steady supply of marine life whose dead remains pile up on the sea floor and are quickly buried. But no one really understands how this organic debris is converted into the liquid hydrocarbon petroleum.

Source rocks are, for the most part, not permeable enough to permit the free and relatively rapid flow of oil—necessary requirements for an oil well. Thus oil is commercially obtained, not from source rocks, but from the so-called *reservoir rocks,* most often sandstone. Reservoir rocks are considerably more permeable strata to which the oil has slowly migrated.

To prevent oil from seeping up and out, its reservoir

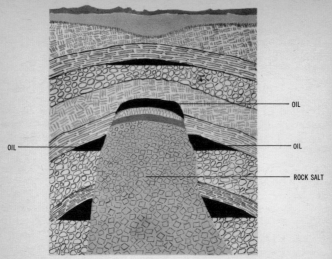

OIL

OIL

OIL

ROCK SALT

Salt domes can serve as structural traps for oil, prohibiting its free migration and keeping it concentrated within a limited area.

rock is topped with a layer of fine-grained rock, like shale, which is virtually impermeable to oil or gas. Such lids are known as *cap rocks*.

In addition to a source rock, a reservoir rock and a cap rock, commercial accumulations of oil require some kind of structural trap to prohibit the free migration of oil and keep it concentrated within a limited area. The most common traps are anticlines and salt domes. Another type is the stratigraphic trap, where the oil lies in an undeformed reservoir rock surrounded by cap rock. And still another trap is a buried organic reef, like a coral reef submerged under later sediments.

The first well dug specifically for oil was completed in August 1859, in Pennsylvania. Originally a highly haphazard endeavor, the search for oil now relies heavily on scientific techniques. Almost all oil companies have geologists on their staffs. It has been estimated that 15,000 of the approximately 20,000 geologists in the United States are working in some phase of the oil industry.

Important sources of oil outside the United States are the vast reserves of the Middle East—at least three times greater than those of the U.S.A.—and the region bordering the Gulf of Mexico and the Carribbean Sea. Other important reserves reside within the continental slopes, but whether their large-scale exploitation is economically practical has yet to be determined.

The most extensive oil field in the world—105 miles long and a few miles wide—is the highly productive El Nala anticline in Saudi Arabia. The single most productive well in history, which yielded 60 million barrels of oil before giving way to salt water, was drilled near Tampico, Mexico.

Ore Deposits A rock mass from which metal can be commercially obtained is called an ore deposit. But few ore deposits contain metals as such. In most cases the metal is combined with other elements, forming ore minerals. The ore minerals, in turn, are associated with useless materials, called gangue minerals. To obtain ore, the ore minerals must first be separated from the gangue minerals. Then the valuable metals must be extracted from the ore minerals. Profitable exploitation of an ore deposit is a function of the quality and quantity of ore, the ease of transportation, the costs of labor and machinery, and the market price.

Ore is produced in a number of ways. In a process called magmatic segregation, early-crystallizing minerals settle near the base of a magma chamber. Compounds of iron, nickel, titanium and other metals have been concentrated in this way.

Ore deposits also result from contact metamorphism. Hot vapors, issuing from an igneous mass that has invaded sedimentary rocks, metamorphose the rock by replacement. Ores of copper, iron and zinc are produced in this way.

The most common ore deposits are found in veins, fissures that have been filled with mineral matter because of cooling, reduced pressure, evaporation or a change in the chemical nature of the depositing solution. An unusually thick vein, or a group of several closely spaced veins, constitutes a lode. Among the many valuable minerals occurring in veins are gold, silver, copper, nickel and lead.

Another source of ore deposits is sedimentary beds.

These may be unusually heavy concentrations of iron ore, found in certain parts of the world. Or, more commonly, they may be placer deposits—an accumulation of heavy metallic minerals like gold, platinum or tin in streams, marine gravels or sands.

Still another type of ore deposit is formed by weathering. This process may leach out worthless minerals, leaving behind concentrations of valuable materials. Or the chemical changes that occur when weathering exposes a portion of an ore body at earth's surface may result in the enrichment of the minerals themselves.

In the United States, more iron is produced in Minnesota than in all the other states together, with the famed Mesabi Range boasting one of the greatest iron deposits in the world.

Copper, of vital importance to the electrical industry, is produced in the United States, Chile, northern Rhodesia, Canada, the Republic of the Congo, the Soviet Union and Japan. The big copper states in this country are Arizona, Utah and Montana.

Lead and zinc are mined in parts of Missouri, Kansas and Oklahoma. The leading producers of gold are South Africa, Canada, the U.S.S.R. and the U.S.A. The Malay Peninsula and Bolivia supply tin, and Canada is the main source of nickel and cobalt.

Non-metallic Resources   Earth's mineral wealth is not restricted to its fuels and metals. There are a number of other extremely valuable mineral resources, some of which are described briefly below.

Many kinds of rocks are used in construction. Granite, and rocks resembling granite, are valuable building stones because of their strength, durability and attractiveness. Other stones used for building and ornamentation are limestone, dolomite and marble. Slate is an important roofing material.

Clay is used primarily for making brick. But fine, pure-grained clay also supplies us with china and porcelain.

Sand and gravel are in great demand for road coverings. Cement and glass also require sand. Lime mixed with sand provides mortar.

Rock salt deposits yield that precious substance, salt.

Gypsum is used in the manufacture of Portland cement, plaster, wallboard and stucco. Nitrates are the source of commercial fertilizers.

The most dazzling of the non-metallic resources are gemstones, whose beauty and rarity and hardness give them a special place in the mineral kingdom. Gems may be found in place, in the cylindrical-shaped diamond "pipes" of South Africa, in the corundum (ruby and sapphire) mines of Burma, in the emerald-studded rock strata of Colombia. But sometimes a rushing stream or a plodding glacier may carry gems far from their point of origin, perhaps to mingle with the silt in river deposits.

Most treasured of the gemstones is the diamond, the only gem composed of a single element—carbon. It is found primarily in India, Brazil and South Africa.

The mineral beryl supplies rich green emeralds. The most beautiful emeralds come from the Muzo mine in Colombia.

Corundum gems are known popularly as sapphires and rubies. Ruby is a name given only to stones of an intense red color, like those lodged in the white chalk of upper Burma. All other corundum gems—even if they are green or pink or colorless—are called sapphires. The best-known sapphires, however, are the blues—the cornflower blues of Kashmir, the indigo blues of Burma, the green-blues of Australia and the inky blues of Siam.

The fuels and metals on which modern civilizations so heavily depend are neither widely distributed nor eternal. They are concentrated within relatively small portions of the earth. They can be so thoroughly exploited that what remains is too deep, too difficult, too expensive for further mining, They can be entirely exhausted, never to be replaced again.

More mineral fuels and metals have been mined in the last 50 years than in all the rest of man's history on earth. Meanwhile, world population is increasing with head-spinning speed, destined to double from three to six billion by the end of the century. How long will the earth's mineral wealth be adequate to meet the needs of an expanding population?

According to reliable estimates, mankind is in no

imminent danger. Coal and petroleum will be available for several hundred years, and metallic ores will be plentiful for almost as long. But eventually, it seems almost certain, the available minerals will be depleted to a point where our standard of living will be threatened, unless revolutionary technological changes can be made.

MAN AS GEOLOGIC AGENT

Man is a mighty agent of geologic change. His presence has altered this planet as surely as wind and water and ice.

He has built lakes by damming streams. He has moved mountains. He has stabilized rivers. He has halted the incursions of the sea with groins and jetties and seawalls, and reclaimed submerged lowlands to serve his needs. He has altered the relationships between the water and the land with his canals and causeways, tunnels and bridges. In the course of his mining activities he has left deep caverns of carved-out earth and high hills of rock debris.

Indeed, man is today so powerful a geologic agent that he can exercise the murderous force of an erupting volcano or a wrenching earthquake. He can, within a few days, mutilate and destroy much of the previous work of the past four or five billion years. But if he is kinder than a glacier, and wiser than an ape, perhaps this peerless planet will endure.

MAJOR STRATIGRAPHIC AND TIME DIVISIONS IN USE BY THE U. S. GEOLOGICAL SURVEY

Era	System or Period	Series or Epoch	Estimated ages of time boundaries in millions of years Holmes[1]	Kulp [2]
Cenozoic	Quaternary	Recent		
		Pleistocene	1	1
	Tertiary	Pliocene	11	13
		Miocene	25	25
		Oligocene	40	36
		Eocene	60	58
		Paleocene	70	63
Mesozoic	Cretaceous[3]	Upper (Late) Lower (Early)	135	135
	Jurassic	Upper (Late) Middle (Middle) Lower (Early)	180	181
	Triassic	Upper (Late) Middle (Middle) Lower (Early)	225	230
Paleozoic[3]	Permian[3]	Upper (Late) Lower (Early)	270	280
	Carboniferous Systems — Pennsylvanian[3]	Upper (Late) Middle (Middle) Lower (Early)		
	Carboniferous Systems — Mississippian[3]	Upper (Late) Lower (Early)	350	345
	Devonian	Upper (Late) Middle (Middle) Lower (Early)	400	405
	Silurian[3]	Upper (Late) Middle (Middle) Lower (Early)	440	425
	Ordovician[3]	Upper (Late) Middle (Middle) Lower (Early)	500	500
	Cambrian[3]	Upper (Late) Middle (Middle) Lower (Early)	600	600?
Precambrian[3]		Informal subdivisions such as upper, middle, and lower, or upper and lower, or younger and older may be used locally.	3,000+	

[1] Age values given are the Holmes time scale (Holmes, A., 1960, A revised geological time scale: Edinburgh Geol. Soc., Trans. v. 17, pt. 3, p. 204).

[2] Ages given are the Kulp time scale (Kulp, J. Laurence, 1961, Geologic time scale: Science, v. 133, no. 3459, p. 1111).

[3] Includes provincial series accepted for use in U. S. Geological Survey reports.

Terms designating time are in parentheses. Informal time terms early, middle, and late may be used for the eras, and for periods where there is no formal subdivision into Early, Middle, and Late, and for epochs. Informal rock terms lower, middle, and upper may be used where there is no formal subdivision of a system or of a series.

GEOLOGIC NAMES COMMITTEE, 1962

BIBLIOGRAPHY

Adams, Frank D. *The Birth and Development of the Geological Sciences*. Dover Publications, 1955.

Ames, Gerald, and Rose Wyler. *The Earth's Story*. Creative Educational Society, 1957.

Baker, Robert H. *Astronomy*. D. Van Nostrand Co., 1964.

Barnett, Lincoln, and the Editorial Staff of *Life*. *The World We Live In*. Time, Inc., 1955.

Bascom, Willard. *Waves and Beaches*. Anchor Books, 1964.

Brown, Howard E., Victor E. Monnett, and J. Willis Stovall. *Introduction to Geology*. Ginn & Co., 1958.

Carrington, Richard. *A Guide to Earth History*. New American Library, 1956.

Chamberlain, Barbara Blau. *These Fragile Outposts: A Geological Look at Cape Cod, Martha's Vineyard and Nantucket*. Natural History Press, 1964.

Clark, Thomas H., and Colin W. Stearn. *The Geological Evolution of North America*. Ronald Press Co., 1960.

Clarke, William D. *Oceans, Streams and Glaciers*. Hart Publishing Co., 1961.

Coombs, D. S. *The Growth of the Geological Sciences*. University of Otago, 1957.

Coon, Carleton S. *The Story of Man*. Alfred A. Knopf, 1962.

Dury, G. H. *The Face of the Earth*. Penguin Books, 1959.

Ehrlich, Paul R., and Richard W. Helm. *The Process of Evolution*. McGraw-Hill, 1963.

Ericson, David B., and Goesta Wollin. *The Deep and the Past*. Alfred A. Knopf, 1964.

Flint, Richard Foster. *Glacial and Pleistocene Geology*. John Wiley & Sons, 1957.

Gamow, George. *A Planet Called Earth*. Viking Press, 1963.

Gilluly, James, A. C. Waters, and A. O. Woodford. *Principles of Geology*. W. H. Freeman & Co., 1959.

Harland, W. B. *The Earth—Rocks, Minerals, and Fossils*. Franklin Watts, 1960.

Holmes, Arthur. *Principles of Physical Geology,* 2d ed. Ronald Press Co., 1965.

Hurlbut, Cornelius S., and Henry E. Wenden. *The Changing Science of Mineralogy*. D. C. Heath & Co., 1964.

Hurley, Patrick M. *How Old Is the Earth?* Anchor Books, 1959.

Kay, Marshall, and Edwin H. Colbert. *Stratigraphy and Life History*. John Wiley & Sons, 1965.

King, Philip B. *The Evolution of North America*. Princeton University Press, 1959.

Kummel, Bernhard. *History of the Earth*. W. H. Freeman & Co., 1961.

Lahee, Frederic H. *Field Geology*. McGraw-Hill, 1961.

Landes, Kenneth K., and Russell C. Hussey. *Geology and Man*. Prentice-Hall, 1948.

Lauber, Patricia. *All About the Ice Age*. Random House, 1959.

MacFall, Russell P. *Collecting Rocks, Minerals, Gems, and Fossils*. Hawthorn Books, 1963.

Mather, Kirtley F. *The Earth Beneath Us*. Random House, 1964.

Milne, Lorus J., and Margery Milne. *The Biotic World and Man*. Prentice-Hall, 1965.

Pearl, Richard M. *Geology*. Barnes & Noble, 1963.

———. *How to Know the Minerals and Rocks*. McGraw-Hill, 1955.

———. *Rocks and Minerals*. Barnes & Noble, 1956.

———. *1001 Questions Answered About Earth Science*. Dodd, Mead & Co., 1962.

Putnam, William C. *Geology*. Oxford University Press, 1964.

Rapport, Samuel, and Helen Wright (eds.). *The Crust of the Earth*. New American Library, 1955.

Romer, Alfred S. *The Vertebrate Story*. University of Chicago Press, 1959.

Savage, J. M. *Evolution*. Holt, Rinehart & Winston, 1963.

Schultz, Gwen. *Glaciers and the Ice Age*. Holt, Rinehart & Winston, 1963.

Shimer, John A. *This Sculptured Earth: The Landscape of America*. Columbia University Press, 1959.

Stewart, Harris B. *The Global Sea*. D. Van Nostrand Co., 1963.

White, Anne Terry. *Rocks All Around Us*. Random House, 1959.

White, J. F. (ed.). *Study of the Earth*. Prentice-Hall, 1962.

Woodbury, David O. *The Great White Mantle*. Viking Press, 1962.

Woodward, Horace B. *History of Geology*. G. P. Putnam's Sons, 1911.

Zumberge, James H. *Elements of Geology*. John Wiley & Sons, 1963.

Index

Abrasion: glacial, 96-98; wind, 107
Abyss, ocean, 128-29
Aggradation, 15
Agricola, G. (G. Bauer), 3
Alluvial fan, 74-75
Amphibole group, 30, 32
Andesite, 34
Anhydrite, 28, 38, 42
Aquifers, 82
Arête, 98-99
Artesian wells, 82-83
Atmosphere, 9-11

Basalt, 13, 32, 37
Batholiths, 133-34
Bauer, G. (G. Agricola), 3
Bed load, 108
Biotite, 25, 29-30, 32-34
Bridges, natural, 71-72, 90
Buttes, 72

Calcite, 22, 28
Canyons, 66
Capacity, stream, 65
Carbonation, 53
Caves, 89
Cementation, 91
Cenozoic era, 215-26
Cinder cones, 138
Cirques, 98
Clay, 129
Cleavage, 25
Cliffs, 70
Coal, 44
Color: of minerals, 20-21; of
    sedimentary rocks, 39
Colorado River, 74, 78
Cols, 99
Competence, stream, 63-65
Composite cones, 139
Concretions, 91
Conglomerate, 38, 39
Continental blocks, 13
Continental glaciers, 96
Continental shelf, 127
Continental slope, 128
Coral reefs, 130-31
Core of earth, 14

Cosmogony, 8
Crater Lake, Ore., 139, 140
Craters, 139
Creep, 57-58
Crust of earth, 12, 13
Crystal form of minerals, 23
Cuestas, 72
Currents, ocean, 116-17

Darwin, C., 131, 176-77
Dating the earth, 180-83
Death Valley, Calif., 74, 162
Deflation, 106-7
Degradation, 15
Deltas, 75
Deluc, J. A., 1
Deposition, 15; desert, 114-15;
    glacial, 101-5; stream, 74-78;
    wave, 124; wind, 109-13
Deserts, 113-15
Diamond, 22, 30
Diastrophism, 15, 145-60
Dikes, 134
Diorite, 32, 34
Discharge: ground-water, 82-87;
    stream, 63
Discontinuity: Mohorovicic (or
    Moho or M=), 12, 13;
    Wiechert-Gutenberg, 12
Dolomite, 28, 43
Drift: non-stratified, 102-3;
    stratified, 104-5
Drumlins, 103
Dunes, sand, 111-13

Earth, the: measurements of, 9;
    structure of, 9-18
Earthflow, 58
Earthquakes, 145-60
Earth's origin: nebular
    hypothesis of, 173;
    planetesimal hypothesis of,
    173; protoplanet hypothesis
    of, 174; tidal hypothesis of,
    173-74
Erosion, 15; in desert, 114;
    glacial, 96-100; ground-water,
    87-90; stream, 65-72; wave,
    121-24; wind, 106-7

...skers, 104-5
...volution of life, 176-77

...aulting of earth, 152-53
...eldspar, 22, 25, 29, 33
...erromagnesian silicates, 30
...jords, 99
...loodplains, 75-78
...luorite, 22, 29
...olding of earth, 146-48
...oliation of rock, 44
...ossils, 2, 3-5, 40, 42, 177-80
...racture, mineral, 25

...abbro, 32, 37
...eochemistry, 7
...eodes, 92
...eodesy, 7
...eologic time scale, 183-84
...eology: branches of, 7-8; and
  man, 230-37; meaning of, 8;
  origin and development of, 1-7;
  processes in, 14-15; in
  unlocking the past, 172-85
...eomorphic cycle, 78-79
...eomorphology, 7
...eophysics, 7-8
...eosyncline, 163
...eysers, 86-87, 92, 144
...lacier National Park, Mont.,
  99, 103
...laciers, 93-105
...neiss, 46-47
...rade, stream, 65
...radient, stream, 62
...rand Canyon, Ariz., 39, 74
...ranite, 13, 25, 32, 33
...ravity, 56-59
...reat Smoky Mts., 40
...round water, 80-92
...ypsum, 22, 28, 38, 42

...alite, 29, 38, 41
...anging valleys, 99
...ardness, 21
...ogbacks, 72
...ooke, R., 5
...orizons, soil, 55
...ornblende, 30, 34
...orns, 99
...ot water deposits, 86-87, 92, 144
...utton, J., 6, 7
...ydration, 52-53
...ydrosphere, 11-12

...ce age, 105
...ce caps, 96
...gneous rock, 31-37
...ntrusive igneous rock, 31, 133-36
...onosphere, 11

Isostasy, 17-18

Kames, 104
Karst topography, 90
Kettles, 102
Knob-and-basin topography, 102

Laccoliths, 134-35
Landslides, 59
Lava, 137
Lava domes, 139
Limestone, 41
Lithification, 39
Lithosphere, 12-15
Load, stream, 63
Loess, 109-11
Luster, 21
Lyell, C., 6, 7

Magma, 31, 132-33
Mantle, 13-14
Marble, 47
Marine deposits, 129-30
Markings on rock, 39-40
Mercalli scale, 157
Mesas, 72
Mesozoic era, 200-14
Metamorphic rock, 44-47
Meteorology, 8
Mica, 29
Mineral fuels, 232-35
Mineralogy, 8
Minerals, 19-30; earth's wealth
  of, 232-38; properties of,
  20-25; rock-forming, 25-30
Mississippi River, 78
Missouri River, 78
Monuments, 72
Moraines, 101, 103
Mountain building: continental
  drift theory of, 167-70;
  contraction theory of, 167;
  convection theory of, 170-71
Mountains, 161-71; Alps, 166;
  Appalachian, 163-66; fault-
  block, 162; fold, 162-63;
  Rocky, 166-67; volcanic, 161-62
Mudflow, 58-59

Obsidian, 32, 34
Ocean basin, 13
Oceanography, 8
Olivine, 30, 32, 37
Ore deposits, 235-36
Orthoclase feldspar, 22, 29, 34
Oxidation, 53

Paleobotany, 8
Paleontology, 8
Paleozoic era, 186-99

Paleozoology, 8
Perched water, 82
Peridotite, 13, 33, 37
Permeability of rock, 81-82
Petrifaction, 92
Petrified Forest National
    Monument, Ariz., 92
Petrology, 7
Piedmont glacier, 94-96
Pikes Peak, Colo., 33
Pillars, 91
Plagioclase feldspar, 29, 34, 37
Pleistocene epoch, 226-29
Porosity of rock, 81
Porphyry, 37
Potholes, 68-70
Pumice, 34
Pyroxene, 32, 34, 37

Quartz, 22, 25, 28, 33, 34
Quartzite, 47

Rapids, 67-68
Regolith, 48
Resources, non-metallic, 236-38
Rhyolite, 32, 33-34
Richter scale, 158
Rock glacier, 59
Rocks, 31-47; igneous, 31-37;
    metamorphic, 44-47;
    sedimentary, 37-44
Run-off, stream, 60

Sand dunes, 111-13
Sandstone, 38, 39
Schist, 46
Sea, 116-31
Seashore, 116-31
Sedimentary rocks, 37-44
Seismic sea waves, 119-21
Seismograph, 156-57
Shale, 38, 41
Sheet erosion, 61
Shield volcanoes, 138
Sierra Nevadas, 34, 162
Sill, 134
Sink holes, 89-90
Slate, 45
Soil, 54-56
Solifluction, 58

Solution, 52
Specific gravity of minerals, 22
Spring, water, 86
Stalactites, 91
Stalagmites, 91
Steno, N., 5
Stocks, 134
Stratification, 39
Stratigraphy, 7
Stratosphere, 10-11
Streak, mineral, 21
Streams, 60-79, 85
Structure, mineral, 24
Suspended load, 108-9

Talus, 59
Tarns, 99
Terraces, 70
Texture, rock, 31-32
Tidal waves, 119-21
Tides, 117-18
Till, 102-3
Transportation: in desert, 114;
    glacial, 100-1; ground-water,
    90-92; stream, 72-74; wave,
    124; wind, 107-9
Troposphere, 10
Tsunamis (waves), 119-21

Valley glaciers, 94
Velocity, stream, 62
Volcanic breccia, 37
Volcanic necks, 136
Volcanic tuff, 37
Volcanoes, 132-44
Vulcanism, 15, 132-44

Warping, 146
Water table, 81
Waterfalls, 67-68
Waves, 118-21
Weathering, 15, 48-54
Wells, water, 82-84
Werner, A., 5
Wind, 106-13

Yellowstone National Park,
    Wyo., 34
Yosemite National Park, Calif.,
    48, 51, 98, 99